THE OFFICIAL BIRMINGHAM CITY QUIZ BOOK

THE OFFICIAL BIRMINGHAM CITY QUIZ BOOK

Compiled by Chris Cowlin and Marc White

Foreword by Alex McLeish

APEX PUBLISHING LTD

First published in hardback in 2009 by
Apex Publishing Ltd
PO Box 7086, Clacton on Sea, Essex, CO15 5WN, England
www.apexpublishing.co.uk

British Library Cataloguing-in-Publication Data
A catalogue record for this book
is available from the British Library

ISBN: 1-906358-67-2   978-1-906358-67-9

Typeset in 10.5pt Chianti Bdlt Win95BT

Cover Design: Siobhan Smith

Printed in Great Britain by the
MPG Books Group, Bodmin and King's Lynn

Author's Note:
Please can you contact me: **ChrisCowlin@btconnect.com** if you find any mistakes/errors in this book as I would like to put them right on any future reprints of this book. I would also like to hear from Blues fans who have enjoyed the test! For more information on me and my books please look at: **www.ChrisCowlin.com**

This book is an official product of Birmingham City Football Club.

We would like to dedicate this book to:

All the players and staff who have worked for the club during their history.

FOREWORD

Hello and welcome to The Official Birmingham City Quiz Book.
Birmingham City is a football club with a great history and tradition.

Here at The Blues we have wonderful supporters who give the players such tremendous backing and once again you've shown just how much you love the club by purchasing this great quiz book.

I'd like you all to 'Keep Right On' with cheering the lads on and when you're not down at St Andrews making a huge noise.

This quiz book is both informative and enjoyable and will certainly have one or two bluenoses scratching their heads! A certain must have for all blues fans! I hope you spend many happy hours enjoying The Official Birmingham City Quiz Book.

Enjoy the book!
Alex McLeish

INTRODUCTION
By Chris Cowlin

I would first of all like to thank Alex McLeish for writing the foreword to this book. I am very grateful for his help on this project and was truly delighted when he agreed to write a few words. I would also like to thank everyone for their comments and reviews (which can be found at the back of the book).

I would also like to thank Wayne Cowen at Birmingham City Football Club for his help and advice during the book's compilation.

I have thoroughly enjoyed working on this book. Up the Blues!

It was great working with Marc White again. I really hope you enjoy this book. Hopefully it should bring back some wonderful memories of this fantastic club!

In closing, I would like to thank all my friends and family for encouraging me to complete this project.

Chris Cowlin.

Best wishes
Chris Cowlin

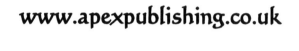
www.apexpublishing.co.uk

CLUB HISTORY & RECORDS

1. In what year was the club formed?

2. True or false: the club was formed by a group of cricketers, known then as Small Heath Alliance?

3. Where were the team placed at the end of the 1955/56 season, their highest ever finishing position in Division 1?

4. Who was Birmingham's manager when the club won the League Cup in 1963?

5. In which two years were Birmingham City FA Cup runners-up?

6. In which Cup were Birmingham City runners-up in 1960 and 1961?

7. By what three names has the club been known since its formation, prior to adopting the name of Birmingham City in 1945?

8. For which centre forward did Birmingham pay a club record transfer fee of £6.25 million during May 2004?

9. Who holds the club record for scoring the most League goals in a season, with 29 goals during 1927/28 in Division 1?

10. What is the club's nickname?

LEAGUE CUP RUNNERS-UP - 2001

11. Which team beat The Blues 5-4 on penalties in the final?

12. Which defender scored a goal for Birmingham in the 90th minute to level the score at 1-1?

13. At which stadium was the final played?

14. Which Birmingham manager guided the club to the final?

15. Can you recall the name of the referee in the final?

16. Which East Anglian team did Birmingham beat 4-2 on aggregate in the semi-finals over the two legs?

17. Which defender scored the winning goal in the 90th minute in a 2-1 win against Newcastle United at St Andrew's in the 4th round?

18. Which Essex team did Birmingham beat 5-0 away from home during August 2000 in the 1st round, 1st leg?

19. Which North London team did Birmingham beat 3-1 away from home in the 3rd round?

20. Following on from the previous question, which Blues striker scored a brace in the game?

MAIK TAYLOR

21. From which club did The Blues sign Maik on loan in August 2003 and then on a permanent basis in March 2004?

22. What is Maik's middle name – Serge, Sean or Stefan?

23. For which country has Maik won full international caps?

24. Against which country did Maik make his full international debut in a 3-0 defeat in 1999?

25. Which Birmingham City manager signed Maik for The Blues?

26. In which year was Maik born in Germany – 1970, 1971 or 1972?

27. For which team did Maik play between 1992 and 1995?

28. True or false: Maik scored a League goal for The Blues during the 2007/08 season?

29. How much did Maik cost Birmingham City when he signed in 2004?

30. In what position does Maik play?

SQUAD NUMBERS 2008/2009 – 1

Match up the player with the squad number he wore during the season

31.	Cameron Jerome	7
32.	Colin Doyle	6
33.	Martin Taylor	13
34.	Liam Ridgewell	21
35.	Jordon Mutch	11
36.	Radhi Jaidi	10
37.	Gary McSheffrey	17
38.	Sebastian Larsson	23
39.	Stuart Parnaby	15
40.	Marcus Bent	5

THE CHAMPIONSHIP RUNNERS-UP – 2006/2007

41. Which Blues manager led the club to this success?

42. Which team denied Birmingham the Championship, winning by 2 points?

43. How many of their 46 League matches did The Blues win – 23, 26 or 29?

44. True or false: Birmingham were unbeaten in their six League matches during December 2006?

45. Which forward scored the winning goal for The Blues in the 2-1 home win on the opening day of the League season against Colchester United?

46. Which Blues player scored a brace in the 3-0 home win against Coventry City during April 2007?

47. Which striker finished as the club's highest League scorer with 13 goals?

48. Can you name the two goalkeepers that played in Birmingham's 46 League matches this season?

49. Who scored the winning goal for Birmingham City in the 88th minute in the 3-2 away win against Wolves during April 2007?

50. Which two teams did Birmingham beat 1-0 away from home during October 2006?

SEBASTIAN LARSSON

51. In which year was Sebastian born – 1983, 1985 or 1987?

52. From which club did Sebastian join Birmingham, initially on loan in 2006 and then on a permanent basis in 2007?

53. Which Blues manager signed Sebastian for Birmingham City?

54. Against which team did Sebastian score his first Blues goal, in the 90th minute in a 2-1 home win during August 2006?

55. How many League goals did Sebastian score for Birmingham City during 2006/07?

56. Against which team did Sebastian score the opening goal in a 1-1 away League draw during August 2008?

57. True or false: Sebastian won the Birmingham Player of the Season award during 2007/08?

58. How many League goals did Sebastian score for Birmingham City during 2007/08?

59. Against which team did Sebastian make his Blues League debut in a 0-0 home draw during August 2006?

60. For which country has Sebastian won full international caps?

MANAGERS

Match up the manager with the year he took over at Birmingham City

61.	Steve Bruce	1989
62.	Lou Macari	2007
63.	Ron Saunders	1996
64.	Terry Cooper	2001
65.	Dave Mackay	1991
66.	Alex McLeish	1987
67.	John Bond	1993
68.	Barry Fry	1982
69.	Garry Pendrey	1991
70.	Trevor Francis	1986

TREVOR FRANCIS - 1

71. Trevor began his professional career with Birmingham City in the early 1970s, making his debut for the club in what year?

72. How old was Trevor when he pulled on a Blues shirt for his professional debut?

73. Against which Welsh 'Bluebirds' did Trevor make his Birmingham City debut, in a 2-0 away defeat?

74. In what year did Trevor leave his beloved St Andrew's?

75. Which club did Trevor join when he left The Blues?

76. Following on from the previous question, it was widely reported in the media that when Trevor joined this team he became British football's first £1 million player. To the nearest £50, what was the actual fee?

77. How many goals did Trevor score in the 22 games he played for The Blues in first season?

78. On 30 October 1976 Trevor scored one of the greatest goals in Birmingham City's history, against which London club in a 2-1 win?

79. In what year was Trevor capped at full international level by England?

80. Following on from the previous question, can you recall the England manager who capped Trevor for the first time?

THE BLUES IN EUROPE

81. In which 1950s season did The Blues first play in one of the major European competitions?

82. Following on from the previous question, in which competition did they participate?

83. Which Yugoslavian side was the first club that Birmingham City played in this European competition, a team that in 2009 play their football in the largest city in Croatia?

84. Following on from the previous question, name the Birmingham City striker (1954-59) who scored the only goal of the game to give The Blues a 1-0 win.

85. The Blues' second game in this European competition saw them draw 0-0 at the San Siro. Name their opponents.

86. Which Welsh wing half scored Birmingham City's first ever home goal in this European competition in a 3-0 home win over the team in Question 83?

87. In what position did The Blues finish in their Group in this competition?

88. How many seasons did this competition take to complete?

89. How far did The Blues progress in this competition?

90. Which Spanish side knocked Birmingham City out of the competition and went on to win the inaugural trophy?

MALCOLM PAGE

91. What is Malcolm's middle name – Ernest, Eric or Edward?

92. For how many seasons was Malcolm a Blues player?

93. How many competitive games did Malcolm play for The Blues in his career – 191, 291 or 391?

94. What was the only honour that Malcolm won as a Blues player?

95. Against which team did Malcolm score for The Blues in a 3-1 home win in the FA Cup quarter-final during March 1972?

96. In what year did Malcolm leave St Andrew's?

97. When Malcolm left The Blues he signed for which club?

98. How many competitive goals did Malcolm score in his Birmingham City career – 8, 10 or 12?

99. For which country did Malcolm win 28 caps during his playing career?

100. In which year was Malcolm born – 1947, 1948 or 1949?

DIVISION 3 RUNNERS-UP – 1991/1992

101. Who was The Blues' manager during this season, guiding the club to 2nd place in the League?

102. True or false: the club lost three of their final four League matches?

103. How many of their 46 League matches did Birmingham City win – 15, 18 or 21?

104. Who scored Birmingham's only goal in the 1-0 away win against West Bromwich Albion during October 1991?

105. Which forward finished the season with 10 goals in 38 starts and 2 substitute appearances?

106. True or false: The Blues never scored more than three goals in a League match during the season?

107. Who was the only player to score a brace for Birmingham this season, in a 3-1 home win against Fulham during December 1991?

108. What was the average home attendance this season – 12,399, 15,399 or 18,399?

109. Who was the only Blues player to play in all 46 League matches this season, also finishing as the club's highest League scorer with 17 goals?

110. True or false: Birmingham won their first four League matches of the season?

FREDDIE GOODWIN

111. On 1 October 1953 Freddie was signed as a trainee from Cheshire Schoolboys by which famous Lancashire side?

112. Following on from the previous question, when Freddie signed for this team they were set to become one of the greatest sides ever and were given a nick name by the press in tribute to their manager. Who was he and what was their nickname?

113. What winners' medal did Freddie win in both 1955/56 and 1956/57?

114. When Freddie left the team in Question 111 he signed for which Yorkshire 'United'?

115. Following on from the previous question, how much did Freddie cost this club - £10,000 or £12,000 or £15,000?

116. Freddie collided with which Welsh legend, a Juventus player from 1957-62, in an FA Cup tie against Cardiff City, causing a triple fracture of his leg and resulting in Freddie's retirement from playing on 1 December 1964.

117. In 1964 Freddie was appointed as player/manager of 'The Iron', who are better known by what name?

118. In what year during the early 1970s did Freddie take charge of Birmingham City?

119. Freddie left which East Sussex coastal club to take charge at St Andrew's, having been their manager from 1968?

120. Freddie was appointed manager of which North American Soccer League 'Kicks' from the 'Twin City' after he left St Andrew's in 1986?

MIKAEL FORSSELL

121. For which country has Mikael won full international caps?

122. Which Blues manager signed Mikael on loan in 2003?

123. How many League goals did Mikael score in his 32 starts for The Blues during 2003/04?

124. In which year was Mikael born in Germany – 1980, 1981 or 1982?

125. How much did Birmingham City pay for Mikael when they signed him on a permanent basis in 2005?

126. Against which team did Mikael score a brace for The Blues in a 2-0 away win in the League Cup 2nd round during September 2005?

127. In which month during 2003/04 did Mikael win the Premier League Player of the Month award?

128. Against which club did Mikael score a hat-trick in a 4-1 home League win during March 2008?

129. Against which team did Mikael score his only Blues goal of the 2006/07 League season, in a 1-0 away win during August 2006?

130. From which London club did Birmingham sign Mikael?

NATIONALITIES

Match up the player with his nationality

131.	Colin Doyle	Jamaican
132.	Stephen Carr	Scottish
133.	Kevin Phillips	Irish
134.	Sebastian Larsson	Welsh
135.	James McFadden	English
136.	Trevor Francis	Australian
137.	Franck Queudrue	Irish
138.	Malcolm Page	Swedish
139.	Michael Johnson	French
140.	Frank Mitchell	English

WHO AM I?

141. I am an ex-Blues striker and was awarded my first four international caps for England by four different England managers.

142. I am a former Birmingham City captain and won the club's Player of the Year award in seasons 1969/70 and 1970/71.

143. Up to the end of the 2008/09 season I was the last player to move clubs between Birmingham City and Aston Villa.

144. I played one game for Scotland at youth level against Wales' youth team in 1945 and scored 30 goals in 117 appearances for Plymouth Argyle, a team I helped to win the Third Division South Championship in 1951/52.

145. I am a former Birmingham defender (1972-81) whose contract with Wolverhampton Wanderers was terminated in 1983, the club citing my failure to turn up for an official team photograph as the reason.

146. I gave the legendary Trevor Francis his debut for The Blues.

147. I am the only World Cup winner to have managed The Blues.

148. Prior to joining Birmingham City I was relegated twice with Notts County during the 1990s.

149. I was a Blues winger and scored 9 times in 39 League appearances when The Blues won promotion from the Division 2 at the end of the 1984/85 season.

150. I am a former Birmingham City midfielder and celebrated my 600th game in charge of my team with a 1-0 victory over The Blues at St Andrew's in September 2005.

DES BREMNER

151. What is Des's middle name – George, Graham or Gavin?

152. For which Scottish team did Des play between 1972 and 1979?

153. In what year did Des leave St Andrew's and join Fulham?

154. Which Blues manager signed Des for the club in September 1984?

155. Against which team did Des make his Blues debut during September 1984 in a 1-0 home win?

156. Des had been at St Andrew's for two years before scoring his first League goal for The Blues, against which team in a 1-1 away draw during September 1986?

157. Against which team did Des score The Blues' winning goal in a 2-1 home win during December 1986?

158. From which team did Des sign to join The Blues in 1984?

159. How many full international caps did Des win for Scotland in his football career?

160. In which year was Des born – 1969, 1970 or 1971?

WHERE DID THEY COME FROM? - 1

Match up the player with the team he
left to join Birmingham City

161.	Marcus Bent	Blackburn Rovers
162.	James McFadden	Tottenham Hotspur
163.	Barry Horne	Charlton Athletic
164.	Martin Grainger	Everton
165.	Gary Ablett	Hibernian
166.	Mario Melchiot	Everton
167.	Darren Anderton	Everton
168.	Dwight Yorke	Brentford
169.	David Murphy	Everton
170.	Lee Carsley	Chelsea

LEAGUE CUP WINNERS - 1963

171.   Which side did The Blues have the satisfaction of
       beating to win the 1963 League Cup final?

172.   Prior to the final, The Blues had lost the most recent
       meeting between the two clubs. Can you recall the
       score?

173.   Name 'The Vikings' that The Blues beat in the first
       game of their successful League Cup winning run in
       season 1962/63.

174.   On 11 December 1962 The Blues beat which
       Lancashire team 6-0, a club that holds the unenviable
       distinction of being the first European trophy winners
       to play in the bottom tier of their country's League
       system?

175.   Name the manager who guided The Blues to Cup
       glory.

176.   Which Blues player, who shares his surname with a
       vegetable, opened the scoring in the 1st leg of the
       final?

177.   Following on from the previous question, which other
       Blues player, who shares his surname with a famous
       Lancashire 'Park', scored in the final?

178.   Name the Lancashire side that The Blues beat in the
       semi-final.

179.   The 2nd leg of the final finished in a draw, but what
       was the score?

180.   The Blues won the League Cup on an aggregate score,
       but what was it?

ALEX GOVAN

181. Alex began his career with 'The Pilgrims', who are better known by what name?

182. In what year during the early 1950s did Alex arrive at St Andrew's?

183. At the age of 18 years old Alex was called up to serve in which part of the Armed Forces?

184. Which Birmingham City manager persuaded Alex to join The Blues?

185. To the nearest £2,000, how much did Birmingham City pay for Alex's services?

186. In which season was Alex the club's leading goalscorer?

187. What was the only winners' medal that Alex won playing for The Blues?

188. In what year during the late 1950s did the popular Govan leave The Blues?

189. Following on from Question 186, which south coast club did Alex join?

190. The end of Alex's Blues career was effectively signalled when the club signed which winger, a player who would himself go on to become a club legend?

FOOTBALL LEAGUE TROPHY WINNERS - 1991

191. Which company sponsored the competition in season 1990/91?

192. The Blues were in the Southern Section Group 6 along with two other teams. Name the team that they beat 1-0 at the Bescot Stadium.

193. Birmingham beat which 'Red Imps' 2-0 at St Andrew's, a result that saw the visitors finish bottom of Group 6?

194. The Blues squeezed past which Welsh side in Round 1, winning a penalty shootout following a 0-0 draw at St Andrew's?

195. Name the 'Town' that Birmingham beat 2-0 at St Andrew's in the South Area quarter-final.

196. In the South Area semi-finals The Blues beat which 'United'?

197. The Blues won both legs of the South Area final, winning 2-1 at home and 1-0 at Griffin Park, against which opponents?

198. Can you name the club that The Blues beat 3-2 in the final?

199. Which ground hosted the 1991 final?

200. Name the manager who guided The Blues to victory in the competition.

MIXED BAG – 1

201. How many points behind the Second Division winners did The Blues finish in runners-up spot in season 1984/85?

202. In what year during the early 1960s did Ray Martin sign for The Blues?

203. Which former Blues player is credited with being responsible for the club's fans adopting Harry Lauder's song 'Keep Right on to the End of the Road' as their anthem?

204. The Blues were the first club to do what in season 1955/56?

205. What is Birmingham City's highest ever finish in the top flight of English football (i.e. Division 1, now known as the Premier League)?

206. In 1984 which player was the last established first-team player to move directly from Aston Villa to Birmingham City?

207. For which London club did Alan Curbishley play between 1984 and 1987?

208. What age was Joe Gallagher when he was appointed captain of Birmingham City?

209. What did Sir John Holder do at St Andrew's on 26 December 1906?

210. Name the popular British boxer who beat Johnny Prescott at St Andrew's in 1965 to retain his British and Empire heavyweight title.

BARRY FRY

211. In what year was Barry appointed manager of The Blues?

212. Which manager took over when Barry left St Andrew's as Blues boss?

213. Which team did Barry manage between 1978 and 1985 and then again between 1986 and 1993?

214. What is Barry's middle name – Francis, Frank or Freddie?

215. True or false: Barry guided The Blues to the Division 2 title in his first full season at the club?

216. Barry took over from which Blues manager?

217. In what position did Barry play during his playing days?

218. In which year was Barry born in Bedford – 1943, 1944 or 1945?

219. Which Essex team did Barry manage before joining The Blues?

220. Which season was Barry's last at St Andrew's?

ALEX McLEISH

221. In which year was Alex born – 1958, 1959 or 1960?

222. What is Alex's nickname?

223. In what position did Alex play during his playing days?

224. How many full international caps did Alex win for Scotland during his career?

225. Which team did Alex manage between 2001 and 2006?

226. In what year was Alex appointed as Birmingham City manager?

227. Which team did Birmingham beat 3-2 away from home during Alex's first game in charge of The Blues?

228. Against which team did Alex guide Birmingham to a 4-1 home win during May 2008 on the final day of the 2007/08 Premier League season?

229. To what position in the Championship did Alex guide The Blues during 2008/09?

230. Which country did Alex manage during 2007?

APPEARANCES – 1

Match up the player with the number of competitive appearances he made for the club in his career

231.	Gary Sprake	153 (2)
232.	Dennis Mortimer	95 (7)
233.	Dave Latchford	25 (4)
234.	Howard Kendall	312
235.	Ted Duckhouse	45 (21)
236.	Alan Curbishley	37
237.	Alan Buckley	239
238.	Steve Lynex	134
239.	Fred Harris	139
240.	Julian Dicks	22

BRIAN ROBERTS

241. True or false: Brian was a goalkeeper during his football career?

242. In which year was Brian born in Manchester – 1953, 1954 or 1955?

243. What was the only honour that Brian won as a Blues player?

244. In what year did Brian join The Blues?

245. From which club did Brian sign to join Birmingham City?

246. Which manager signed Brian for The Blues?

247. How many League appearances did Brian make for Birmingham City during his career – 187, 189 or 191?

248. Brian was most commonly known by which nickname?

249. True or false: Brian didn't score a League goal for The Blues in his career?

250. For which Midlands club did Brian sign when he left St Andrew's in 1990?

RON SAUNDERS

251. Ron took over The Blues management hot seat from which manager in February 1982?

252. In what position did the club finish in Division 1 during 1982/83, Ron's first full season in charge at St Andrew's?

253. In what position did Ron play during his playing days?

254. True or false: Ron managed rivals Aston Villa before being appointed as Blues boss?

255. Ron was the first ever manager in football history to do what?

256. What was the only honour that Ron won as a Blues manager?

257. Ron ended his managerial career in 1987 at which club?

258. In which year was Ron born in Birkenhead – 1930, 1931 or 1932?

259. True or false: Ron played for The Blues during his career?

260. Who was appointed as Blues manager when Ron left the club in January 1986?

MATTHEW UPSON

261.   What is Matthew's middle name – James, Jason or Jeremy?

262.   In what position does Matthew play?

263.   From which London team did Matthew sign in 2003 to join The Blues?

264.   How many League goals did Matthew score for The Blues in his eight appearances during the 2006/07 season?

265.   Which London team did Matthew join in January 2007 when he left St Andrew's?

266.   Against which team did Matthew score his first Blues goal, Birmingham's second goal in a 2-2 home draw during October 2004?

267.   Against which team did Matthew play during his Blues League debut, in a 4-2 away defeat during February 2003?

268.   Which Blues manager signed Matthew for Birmingham City?

269.   Against which country did Matthew score for England in a 2-1 win during November 2008, also winning the ITV Match of the Match award?

270.   At which club did Matthew start his professional football career in 1996?

271. The Blues won Division 2 in 1995 when Michael Jackson had the UK Christmas No.1 with which song?

272. The Blues finished in 5th place in Division 2 in 2002 when which group had the UK Christmas No. 1 with 'Sorry Seems to be the Hardest Word'?

273. The Blues finished in 13th place in the Premier League when Kelly and Ozzy Osbourne had the UK Christmas No. 1 with 'Changes'. What was the year?

274. The Blues were relegated to Division 2 in 1986 when the Housemartins had the UK Christmas No. 1 with which song?

275. The Blues finished in 20th place in Division 4 when Queen had the UK Christmas No. 1 with 'Bohemian Rhapsody/These are the Days of Our Lives'. What was the year?

276. The Blues finished in 12th place in Division 1 in 1999 when which group had the UK Christmas No. 1 hit with 'I Have a Dream/Seasons in the Sun'?

277. The Blues finished second from bottom of Division 1 and were relegated to Division 2 when Pink Floyd had the UK Christmas No. 1 with 'Another Brick in the Wall'. What was the year?

278. The Blues finished in 9th place in Division 2 in 1971 when Benny Hill had the UK Christmas No. 1 with which song?

279. The Blues finished as runners-up in Division 2 in 1972 and were promoted to Division 1 when which singer had the UK Christmas No. 1 with 'Long Haired Lover from Liverpool'?

280. The Blues finished in 18th place in Division 2 when Dave Edmunds had the UK Christmas No. 1 with 'I Hear You Knocking'. What was the year?

FOOTBALL LEAGUE TROPHY
WINNERS - 1995

281.   Name the manager who guided The Blues to Cup glory.

282.   Which company sponsored the Cup in season 1994/95?

283.   The Blues won their opening game in Group 7 of the Southern Section 5-3 at London Road, against which team?

284.   Birmingham had a 3-0 win at St Andrew's against 'The Saddlers', who are better known by what name?

285.   Which side did The Blues defeat 1-0 in round 2 of the Southern Section?

286.   Birmingham had a 3-1 victory in the Southern quarter-finals over 'The Bulls', who are better known by what name?

287.   In the Southern Area semi-finals The Blues narrowly beat which Welsh side 3-2 after extra time?

288.   Which London side did The Blues beat 1-0 at home and 3-2 away in the two legs of the Southern Area final?

289.   The Blues beat which 'United' at Wembley Stadium in the final?

290.   Following on from the previous question, what was the score in the final after playing extra time to decide the winner?

2008/2009

291. Name the Yorkshire outfit that The Blues beat 1-0 at St Andrew's on the opening day of the season.

292. Following on from the previous question, which player made a dream debut for The Blues, scoring in the last minute to secure all three points?

293. Birmingham were dumped out of the League Cup at St Mary's Stadium by a team that began life as St Mary's YMA in 1885. Name them.

294. On Boxing Day 2008 The Blues beat 'The Tractor Boys' 1-0 away. By what name are they better known?

295. Birmingham won their opening Carling Cup game with a comfortable 4-0 win at Adams Park, the home of which 'Wanderers'?

296. The Blues won 2-1 away and drew 1-1 at home with a side that are the only team to have taken the FA Cup out of England. Name them.

297. The Blues lost their first League game of the season 1-0 at home to a seaside team that began life in 1877 as Victoria Football Club. Who are they?

298. The Blues went out of the FA Cup after losing 2-0 at home to a team that led the Championship table at the time. Who are they?

299. Name the on-loan midfielder who scored The Blues' first goal of 2009 in a match that marked his debut for the club.

300. Which former European Cup winners did The Blues beat 2-0 in the League at St Andrew's on 14 February 2009?

STEVE BRUCE

301. What is Steve's middle name – Roger, Richard or Rick?

302. In what position did Steve play in his playing days?

303. At which club did Steve start his managerial career, during the 1998/99 season?

304. Steve was appointed as Birmingham City manager in 2001, but which other two teams did Steve manage this year?

305. The Blues lost 2-1 away to which team in Steve's first match in charge of Birmingham City during December 2001?

306. True or false: Steve won promotion with Birmingham City during his first season at St Andrew's?

307. True or false: Steve won a full international cap for England during his career?

308. Can you name the title of Steve's autobiography?

309. In addition to his autobiography Steve has penned three novels. Can you name the title of one of them?

310. At which club was Steve appointed manager in 2007?

STEPHEN CLEMENCE

311. From which club did Stephen sign in 2003 to join The Blues?

312. How many League goals did Stephen score for Birmingham City during his football career – 8, 18 or 28?

313. Who is Stephen's famous goalkeeping father, having played for Liverpool and Tottenham?

314. In which year was Stephen born in Liverpool – 1976, 1977 or 1978?

315. True or false: Stephen made his Blues debut in a 4-0 home defeat to Arsenal?

316. Against which club did Stephen score his first Blues goal, in a 2-1 home win during February 2003?

317. Stephen scored for Birmingham in a 3-0 home win against Middlesbrough during April 2003, but who were the other Blues scorers?

318. Which club did Stephen join when he left St Andrew's in July 2007?

319. Can you name the Sky One soap opera in which Stephen's wife Angela starred as character Tash Parker?

320. What is Stephen's middle name – Noel, Neal or Niall?

JEFF KENNA

321. What is Jeff's middle name – Jude, Joseph or Jacob?

322. How many full international caps did Jeff win for the Republic of Ireland?

323. In which year was Jeff born – 1969, 1970 or 1971?

324. For which team did Jeff play between 1995 and 2002?

325. In what year did Jeff sign for The Blues, initially on loan and then permanently?

326. Jeff was appointed manager of which Irish football club in January 2009?

327. How many League goals did Jeff score in his Birmingham City career?

328. Against which London side did Jeff score The Blues' equaliser in the 68th minute in a 1-1 home draw during November 2002?

329. Against which team did Jeff make his Blues debut, while on loan, in a 1-0 away win on Boxing Day 2001?

330. For which club did Jeff sign in March 2004 when he left St Andrew's?

POSITIONS IN THE LEAGUE – 1

Match up the season with Birmingham City's
finishing position in the League

331.	1991/1992	10th in Division 1
332.	1992/1993	15th in Division 1
333.	1993/1994	4th in Division 1
334.	1994/1995	5th in Division 1
335.	1995/1996	5th in Division 1
336.	1996/1997	1st in Division 2
337.	1997/1998	2nd in Division 3
338.	1998/1999	7th in Division 1
339.	1999/2000	19th in Division 2
340.	2000/2001	22nd in Division 1

DAMIEN JOHNSON

341. What is Damien's middle name – Martin, Mark or Michael?

342. For which country is Damien a full international?

343. From which club did Damien join The Blues in March 2002?

344. What Blues squad number did Damien wear during the 2008/09 season?

345. Which Blues manager signed Damien and handed him his debut for the club?

346. Against which team did Damien make his Blues debut, in a 3-1 away win during March 2002?

347. Against which Yorkshire team did Damien score his only League goal for The Blues during 2002/03, potting the winner in the 58th minute in a 2-1 home win in August 2002?

348. Against which team did Damien score The Blues' opening goal in a 3-0 home win in the Premier League during February 2004?

349. In which year was Damien born - 1978, 1979 or 1980?

350. How many League appearances did Damien make for The Blues during the 2008/09 season – 9, 19 or 29?

LIAM RIDGEWELL

351. In what year did Liam sign for The Blues from Aston Villa?

352. What Blues squad number did Liam wear during 2008/09?

353. Which manager signed Liam for Birmingham City?

354. How many England Under-21 caps did Liam win during his career – 7, 8 or 9?

355. Which Plymouth Argyle midfielder challenged Liam in a match during April 2009, resulting in Liam breaking his leg?

356. In which year was Liam born - 1983, 1984 or 1985?

357. What is Liam's middle name – Matthew, Luke or John?

358. How much did Liam cost The Blues?

359. Against which club did Liam score in a 2-1 home League win during November 2008?

360. Against which team did Liam score his first Blues goal in a 3-2 home Premier League win during October 2007?

MIXED BAG - 2

361. During their successful promotion-winning season in 1984/85 The Blues lost 1-0 away in the League to which Lancashire side?

362. When Ray Martin was awarded a Testimonial in 1971 the opposition that day were his hometown club. Name the Black Country outfit.

363. In 1987/88, which 'Seagulls' did Alan Curbishley help to win promotion to the Second Division as Third Division runners-up in his first season at the club?

364. In season 1956/57 The Blues' top goalscorer was speedy winger Alex Govan with an incredible 30 goals, but how many hat-tricks did he notch up?

365. Ex-Blues legend Joe Gallagher played for two teams that, along with Preston North End, are the only clubs in the history of English football to win all four of the Football League's top divisions – Division 1 (now The Premier League), Division 2 (now The Championship), Division 3 (now League 1) and Division 4 (now League 2). Name both teams.

366. Which boxer, who shares his name with a famous high wayman, is reputedly the first black fighter to have won a British boxing title, in 1949 defeating Albert Finch at St Andrew's to retain his British and Empire middleweight titles?

367. St Andrew's was the first ground in the history of the FA Cup to host what?

368. Following on from the previous question, can you name 'The Potters' that Birmingham beat?

369. After leaving The Blues for a second time in 1991, which player ended up playing for Shrewsbury Town, Hong Kong, Colchester United and Solihull Borough?

370. Which former Blues manager from the 1970s is known for introducing yoga, psychological testing and other new training techniques at the club?

IAN BENNETT

371. At which London club did Ian begin his professional playing career in 1988?

372. For which north-east club did Ian sign in 1989?

373. In what year during the early 1990s did Ian arrive at St Andrew's?

374. From what club did The Blues purchase Ian?

375. Following on from the previous question, the Blues boss that signed Ian went on to manage Ian's former club. Name him.

376. To the nearest £50,000, how much did Birmingham City pay for Ian?

377. Name either of the two teams that Ian joined on loan during his time at St Andrew's.

378. In what year did Ian leave The Blues, having made a total of 287 League appearances for the club?

379. Ian signed for which 'United' when he left St Andrew's?

380. At what club, a team he had played for previously, did Ian end his professional playing career in the summer of 2006?

JULIAN DICKS

381. In what year did Julian begin his professional playing career with Birmingham City?

382. What was Julian's nickname, which reflected his 'hard man' tag – The Beast, The Enforcer or The Terminator?

383. Can you recall the year that Julian left St Andrew's?

384. Which team did Julian join after leaving The Blues?

385. To the nearest £50,000, how much did Birmingham City receive for Julian's services?

386. Name the Lancashire side that Ian signed for in 1993.

387. Following on from the previous question, what was Julian the last player to do at this club?

388. Name the future Birmingham City left back (2000-01) who was offered along with Mike Marsh as part of Julian's transfer deal with the club in Question 386.

389. Julian made a welcome return to which one of his former clubs in 1994?

390. Julian ended his career with which Island 'Gulls' in season 2001/02?

WHERE DID THEY GO? - 1

Match up the player with the team he joined on leaving Birmingham City

391.	Jeff Kenna	West Bromwich Albion
392.	Geoff Horsfield	Reading
393.	Darren Purse	Barnsley
394.	Jon McCarthy	Bolton Wanderers
395.	Paul Furlong	Bristol Rovers
396.	Danny Sonner	Derby County
397.	Nick Forster	Wigan Athletic
398.	Kevin Poole	Walsall
399.	Graham Hyde	Queens Park Rangers
400.	Tony Rees	Port Vale

JOHN GAYLE

401. Name either one of John's two jobs before he became a professional footballer.

402. In 1988 John joined his hometown 'Rovers'. Name them.

403. John signed for which reigning FA Cup holders in March 1989?

404. Following on from the previous question, in what year did John leave this club to became a Blue?

405. To the nearest £50,000, how much did The Blues pay for John's services?

406. Name the 'Sky Blues' that John joined when he left Birmingham City in 1993.

407. Following on from the previous question, John only stayed with this team for one season before moving on to Turf Moor, the home of which Lancashire club?

408. John played for which 'United' for one season, 2000/01?

409. For which club, whose name begins with and ends with the same letter, did John play from 1997 to 1998?

410. John ended his career with which 'colourful' Solihull-based non-League side in season 2001/02?

DIVISION TWO CHAMPIONS – 1994/1995

411.   By how many points did The Blues win the title – 1, 4 or 7?

412.   Which side finished as runners-up to Birmingham City in the table, thus also winning promotion to League Division 1?

413.   The Blues were beaten 2-1 away on the opening day of the season by which London outfit?

414.   Birmingham City was eliminated from the League Cup by a team that went on to win the Premier League in season 1994/95. Name them.

415.   Which non-League 'Town' opted to play their 'home' FA Cup tie with The Blues at St Andrew's and lost 4-0?

416.   The Blues hammered which seaside club 7-1 at St Andrew's on New Year's Eve 1994, securing their position at the top of the League?

417.   Name the Blues manager who guided the team to Championship glory.

418.   The Blues beat which Yorkshire 'Town' 2-1 away in the final game of the season?

419.   Which Premier League side put The Blues out of the FA Cup, winning a penalty shootout 2-0 after a 1-1 draw at their own ground?

420.   What happened at the end of the season at the foot of the table for the first time in the history of English football?

GEOFF HORSFIELD

421. In which year was Geoff born in Barnsley – 1972, 1973 or 1974?

422. Which manager signed Geoff for The Blues?

423. How many League goals did Geoff score for Birmingham City in his career – 23, 33 or 43?

424. Did Geoff score his first goal for The Blues on his 3rd, 4th or 5th League appearance for the club?

425. Against which team did Geoff score his first Birmingham City goal, a 61st-minute equaliser, in a 1-1 away draw during September 2000?

426. How many League goals did Geoff score for The Blues during the club's 2002/03 Premier League season – 5, 7 or 9?

427. From which London club did Geoff sign to join The Blues in 2000?

428. Which two honours did Geoff win while at St Andrews?

429. In which position did Geoff play during his career?

430. What is Geoff's middle name – Malcolm, Martin or Mark?

POSITIONS IN THE LEAGUE – 2

*Match up the season with Birmingham City's
finishing position in the League*

431.   1967/1968   11th in Division 1

432.   1969/1970   16th in Division 1

433.   1971/1972   20th in Division 1

434.   1973/1974   3rd in Division 2

435.   1975/1976   21st in Division 1

436.   1977/1978   2nd in Division 2

437.   1979/1980   19th in Division 1

438.   1981/1982   18th in Division 2

439.   1983/1984   19th in Division 1

440.   1985/1986   4th in Division 2

MIXED BAG – 3

441. Which Blues defender was the first Tunisian player to join a Premier League club when he signed for Bolton Wanderers in 2004?

442. Name the Dutch midfielder that The Blues took on loan from AZ Alkmaar for season 2008/09 with an option to purchase the player at the end of the season for a fee of €2 million.

443. Which player, who was on loan to The Blues in season 2008/09, in April 2005 was involved in an on-pitch brawl with his Newcastle United teammate Kieron Dyer in their Premiership game against Aston Villa?

444. Including the 2008/09 competition, how many FA Cup semi-final replays have been played at St Andrew's?

445. Name the Birmingham City manager who sold Robert Hopkins in 1986 to the team he managed from 1980 to 1983.

446. Who was Birmingham's club captain in season 2008/09?

447. Ron Saunders, who guided The Blues to promotion to Division 1 after the team achieved a runners-up position in Division 2 in season 1984/85, had a cameo role in a 1981 episode of which popular ITV soap opera?

448. When legendary Alex Govan arrived at St Andrew's in 1953 he was given what job so that he could avoid National Service (although he later served in the RAF)?

449. Which player won 98 international caps for Ecuador before joining The Blues as a defender in season 2008/09?

450. Alan Curbishley was hotly tipped to fill what future managerial vacancy when the existing manager decided that he would be stepping down from his position in the summer of 2006?

PAUL TAIT

451. In what year did Paul achieve his boyhood dream of signing for The Blues?

452. Paul scored the only goal for Birmingham City in a 1-0 win in which final?

453. Following on from the previous question, after Paul scored he famously revealed the T-shirt he was wearing under his football jersey, bearing a derogatory remark aimed at which rival club?

454. Following on again, how many weeks' wages was Paul fined for this incident?

455. Paul was sent on loan by The Blues to which London club in 1994?

456. During the 1997/98 season Paul was on loan to which 'Town'?

457. In what year did Paul leave Birmingham City?

458. Name the 'United' that Paul joined when he left St Andrew's.

459. To the nearest 30, how many League appearances did Paul make for The Blues?

460. At the end of his career Paul played for an eastern Mediterranean team called Nea Salamis FC. Where are they based?

MIXED BAG – 4

461. Which future Blues manager was at Manchester United when the fateful Munich Air Disaster claimed the lives of eight of his teammates on 6 February 1958?

462. Which Birmingham striker won the first of his 10 international caps for Scotland in a 2002 friendly against Canada and won his last cap in September 2003 against the Faroe Islands in a Euro 2004 qualifying game?

463. Which player, who joined The Blues in March 2009, was initially given squad number 27 but had to be issued with different number, 36, instead, and why?

464. Who is the only Birmingham City player to have captained a country in the 2008 African Cup of Nations?

465. Alan Curbishley returned to which club as player/coach under the management of Lennie Lawrence in 1990?

466. Which season 2008/09 Blues defender told Blues Magazine that the blond streak in his hair was to identify himself to the fans and to show his difference in attitude to the other players?

467. Which season 2008/09 Blues fullback represented his country at schoolboy, youth, under-18, under-21 and full international levels?

468. Who scored Birmingham's goal of the season against Sheffield Wednesday in April 2007, having run half the length of the pitch with the ball before scoring from inside the penalty box?

469. The Blues allowed which Polish goalkeeper to join Motherwell on loan in January 2009 for the rest of the 2008/09 season?

470. Alex Govan was the first player to sing the Blues anthem 'Keep Right on to the End of the Road' on the way to Birmingham's 1956 FA Cup quarter-final 3-1 win against which London side?

MICHAEL JOHNSON

471. How many League goals did Michael score in his Birmingham City career – 12, 24 or 36?

472. What nationality is Michael?

473. How many full international caps did Michael win for his country in his career – 8, 10 or 12?

474. For which club did Michael sign when he left St Andrew's in 2003?

475. What nickname did Michael pick up during his time at St Andrew's?

476. How many League goals did Michael score for The Blues during 1997/98?

477. Against which team did Michael score The Blues' winner in a 2-1 home win in the League Cup 4th round during November 2000?

478. What is Michael's middle name – Owen, Ossie or Oscar?

479. Which Blues manager signed Michael for the club?

480. From which club did Michael sign to join The Blues in September 1995, returning to that team in 2008?

ALBERTO TARANTINI

481. What nationality is Alberto?

482. At which 'Juniors' did Alberto begin his professional playing career in 1973?

483. Following on from the previous question, while with this team Alberto was given the nickname 'Conejo' because of his afro-style hair and large front teeth. What does this word mean in English?

484. What winners' medal did Alberto win in 1978?

485. In what year did Alberto arrive at St Andrew's?

486. To the nearest £50,000, how much did The Blues pay for Alberto's services?

487. Name the Blues manager who brought Alberto to St Andrew's.

488. Alberto made his debut for The Blues in a 1-0 away defeat against which London outfit?

489. Alberto once flattened which Manchester United midfielder on the pitch, whose older brother played for The Blues in season 1968/69?

490. In what year did Alberto leave St Andrew's?

BIRMINGHAM CITY
V. ASTON VILLA - 1

491. The Birmingham City versus Aston Villa derby game is known as what?

492. In what year during the late 1870s did the clubs first meet?

493. Following on from the previous question, what was the score of their first encounter, a win for The Blues?

494. What was significant about the derby game that took place on 1 September 1894?

495. One of the most famous derby games was played at Villa Park on 17 October 1925 in Division 1. What was the score of the game with 11 minutes to go, before The Blues rallied to earn a draw?

496. The Blues recorded their highest ever derby victory on 21 September 1968 at St Andrew's. What was the score?

497. In what season did the pair meet in a Premier League game for the first time?

498. Following on from the previous question, The Blues won both games, but can you recall either of the scores?

499. Up to the end of the 2008/09 season and to the nearest 20, how many first-class competitive meetings have taken place between the two sides?

500. What was significant about the derby game that took place on 16 September 1905?

LEGENDS

Rearrange the letters to reveal the name
of a Birmingham City legend

501. GLI RECKRIM

502. YAR INTARM

503. NEK ENREG

504. EJO DARFDORB

505. AIN TENTNEB

506. DERF RARISH

507. ORY WASHURRT

508. INSEND NENNJIGS

509. YNKEN SNURB

510. LANA HERBYSULIC

GOALSCORERS – 1

Match up the player with the number of competitive goals he scored for the club

511.	Andy Kennedy	35
512.	Pat Van Den Hauwe	73
513.	Alan Ainscow	5
514.	Bob Hatton	2
515.	Roger Hynd	11
516.	Jack Mulraney	1
517.	George Parris	4
518.	David Rennie	22
519.	Steve Whitton	21
520.	Peter Withe	16

THE CHAMPIONSHIP – PLAY-OFF WINNERS – 2001/2002

521. Name the team managed by Kevin Keegan that won League 1.

522. Who were the League's sponsors in season 2001/02?

523. Against which London club did The Blues record their opening win of the season, beating them 4-0 at St Andrew's on 19 August 2001?

524. Name the Lancashire outfit that ended Birmingham City's FA Cup dreams, with the Blues losing 3-0.

525. Which 'United' did Birmingham City beat 2-0 at St Andrew's in their final League game of the season?

526. Which team did The Blues defeat 2-1 on aggregate to reach the play-off final?

527. Can you name the club that The Blues beat in the play-off final?

528. Following on from the previous question, what was the score of the game, which went into extra time after 90 minutes of play?

529. Can you name any Birmingham City player who scored in the play-off final?

530. How many years had it been since The Blues had last played in the top flight of English football?

FORMER AWAY GROUNDS

531.   If The Blues had paid a visit to Maine Road in the past, what team would have been the home side?

532.   If The Blues had paid a visit to Filbert Street in the past, what team would have been the home side?

533.   If The Blues had paid a visit to Roker Park in the past, what team would have been the home side?

534.   If The Blues had paid a visit to Ayresome Park in the past, what team would have been the home side?

535.   If The Blues had paid a visit to Plough Lane in the past, what team would have been the home side?

536.   If The Blues had paid a visit to The Goldstone Ground in the past, what team would have been the home side?

537.   If The Blues had paid a visit to Highfield Road in the past, what team would have been the home side?

538.   If The Blues had paid a visit to The Dell in the past, what team would have been the home side?

539.   If The Blues had paid a visit to Elm Park in the past, what team would have been the home side?

540.   If The Blues had paid a visit to The Baseball Ground in the past, what team would have been the home side?

PAUL FURLONG

541. Name the non-League London side where Paul began his career in 1988, a club that went into administration in June 2007 and was then re-formed under a new name with a year in its title.

542. In 1991 Paul was transferred to which 'City'?

543. In what year did Paul arrive at St Andrew's?

544. From which club did The Blues purchase Paul?

545. Paul made his Blues debut against which London club?

546. To the nearest £250,000, how much did Birmingham City pay for Paul's services?

547. Paul was sent on loan to which 'United' during his Birmingham City career?

548. When Paul left St Andrew's in 2002 which club did he join?

549. In season 2007/08 Paul played for 'The Hatters', who are better known by what name?

550. In January 2009 Paul went on loan to a team that used to be managed by former Blues boss Barry Fry. Which side did he join?

TREVOR FRANCIS - 2

551. In what year did Trevor win a European Cup winners' medal with Nottingham Forest?

552. Following on from the previous question, against which Swedish club did Trevor score the only goal of the game in the final?

553. What was the venue for the 1974 FIFA World Cup final, where Trevor scored the winning goal in the 1980 European Cup final?

554. Name Trevor's Nottingham Forest teammate Martin O'Neill's assistant at rivals Aston Villa in season 2008/09, who supplied the cross for Trevor to score the goal in Question 552 with a header.

555. Trevor played alongside which legendary Dutch striker for the Detroit Express in the North American Soccer League?

556. Trevor played for Nottingham Forest in the 1980 League Cup final but was on the losing side. Name the Midlands team that lifted the trophy.

557. Which Lancashire outfit did Trevor join when he left Nottingham Forest in 1981?

558. Following on from the previous question, name the future Birmingham City manager who signed Trevor for this club.

559. What was the first Italian club that Trevor signed for in 1982?

560. Following on from the previous question, what trophy did Trevor win with this club?

MIXED BAG – 5

561. The Blues squeezed past which Yorkshire club, winning 4-2 at St Andrew's on New Year's Day 1985, en route to gaining promotion to the First Division?

562. In what year during the 1970s did the legendary Ray Martin leave St Andrew's, having played his entire professional career for The Blues?

563. Which future Blues legend won a Third Division South Championship winners' medal in 1951/52 and a Third Division winners' medal in 1958/59 with the club where he began his professional playing career?

564. Following on from the previous question, in what season during the 1950s did The Blues achieve this finish?

565. Name the Algerian international winger that The Blues signed on loan from Fulham in season 2008/09.

566. Which legendary Birmingham City defender was capped by the England 'B' team in a 1-0 win versus Australia at St Andrew's in season 1980/81?

567. Name the 'expensive-sounding' player that The Blues signed on loan from the Polish side GKS Bełchatów in January 2009.

568. Which season 2008/09 Birmingham City defender won a League Cup winners' medal with Tottenham Hotspur in 1999?

569. Which Blues defender played in the 2006 UEFA Cup final for Middlesbrough?

570. On 10 February 2009 a Mali international joined The Blues from Portsmouth on a three-month loan. Who is he?

HOWARD KENDALL

571. Howard joined which Lancashire club, whose home ground is Deepdale, as an apprentice in 1961, turning professional in May 1963 and playing for them in the 1964 FA Cup final?

572. What FA Cup record at the time did Howard set in the 1964 FA Cup final versus West Ham United?

573. What club did Howard sign for in 1967, helping them win the First Division Championship in season 1969/70?

574. Following on from the previous question, in this team Howard formed a formidable midfield partnership with Alan Ball and Colin Harvey. What nickname was given to the talented trio?

575. In what year did Howard arrive at St Andrew's?

576. To the nearest 30, how many League games did Howard play for The Blues?

577. In 1979 which 'Rovers' gave Howard his first taste of management when they appointed him as their player/manager?

578. Howard managed which Spanish side between 1987 and 1989?

579. Can you name the club that Howard managed in three different spells?

580. Howard was the last English manager to do what?

BIRMINGHAM CITY
V. WEST BROMWICH ALBION

581. In what season during the 1880s did the two sides first meet?

582. Following on from the previous question, can you recall in which competition they met?

583. What was the score in the two teams' first encounter?

584. Up to and including the 2008/09 season, in what season did the two clubs last meet in a competitive fixture?

585. Following on from the previous question, this game ended in a draw but what was the final score?

586. What is Birmingham's highest winning margin in a game involving the two rivals?

587. Can you recall The Blues' worst ever loss in a Birmingham City versus WBA derby game – 7-1, 9-1 or 11-1?

588. To the nearest 20, how many times have the clubs faced one another in a competitive match?

589. The Blues recorded their first win over their close rivals after how many encounters?

590. Following on from Question 584, who was the last Birmingham City player to score for The Blues in a derby game against WBA?

GOALSCORERS – 2

Match up the player with the number of competitive goals he scored for the club

591.	Billy Wright	33
592.	Mark Sale	7
593.	Dai Richards	1
594.	Steve McGavin	42
595.	Martin Kuhl	14
596.	Robert Hopkins	2
597.	Nigel Gleghorn	23
598.	Barry Bridges	6
599.	Bert Murray	3
600.	Phil Sproson	46

MARTIN GRAINGER

601. With which Essex team did Martin start his football career?

602. How many League goals did Martin score for Birmingham City during his career – 25, 30 or 35?

603. In which year was Martin born – 1972, 1973 or 1974?

604. From which club did Martin join The Blues in March 1996?

605. Martin was appointed manager of which club on 10 January 2008, only to leave them just 48 hours later?

606. What is Martin's middle name – Robert, Robin or Roger?

607. In what position did Martin playing during his playing days?

608. What award did Martin win at St Andrew's at the end of the 1999/2000 season?

609. Against which club did Martin score The Blues' opening goal after 2 minutes, in a 2-1 home League win during August 2001?

610. Against which team did Martin score in Birmingham's 7-1 away League win during December 1998?

CHRISTOPHE DUGARRY

611.   Can you name the French club where Christophe began his career in 1988?

612.   Following on from the previous question, in what year did Christophe leave this team?

613.   Following on again, name the Italian Serie A side he then joined.

614.   Name the Spanish club that Christophe joined in 1997, staying with them for just one year.

615.   In what year did Christophe sign for The Blues?

616.   Can you name the French club that Christophe played for between 1998 and 2000?

617.   Apart from winning the Spanish Championship (La Liga) in season 1997/98, what other winners' medal did Christophe collect in 1998?

618.   Following on from the previous question, what else did Christophe win with this team?

619.   In what year did Christophe leave St Andrew's?

620.   When Christophe left The Blues he joined which Arab emirate club based in Doha?

MICK HARFORD

621. Mick began his career with which 'City' in 1977, staying with them for three seasons?

622. Mick was born in Sunderland and in 1980 signed for which north-east club?

623. In what year during the early 1980s did Mick arrive at St Andrew's?

624. To the nearest £25,000, how much did The Blues pay for Mick's services?

625. Can you name the Ashton Gate club that Mick left to join Birmingham City?

626. When Mick left The Blues in 1984 he joined which 'Town'?

627. In 1992/93 Mick played for a London-based outfit. Name them.

628. In August 1994 Mick made his last move as a footballer and joined 'The Crazy Gang', who are better known as which club?

629. Which club, former European Cup winners, made Mick their caretaker boss in season 2004/05?

630. Mick was appointed as manager of which one of his many former clubs in 2008?

PAUL DEVLIN

631. At which famous 'County' did Paul begin his professional playing career in 1992?

632. In what year did Paul first sign for The Blues?

633. Following on from the previous question and to the nearest £50,000, how much did The Blues pay for Paul's services?

634. How many total games, covering all competitions, did Paul play for Birmingham City in his three spells (including one spell on loan) at St Andrew's – 123, 153 or 183?

635. Following on from the previous question, how many times did Paul score in those games – 27, 32 or 37?

636. In what year did Paul first leave Birmingham City?

637. When Paul left St Andrew's for the first time which Yorkshire club did he join?

638. Name the manager who brought Paul back to St Andrew's in February 2002.

639. In what year did Paul leave The Blues for the second time?

640. Following on from the previous question, Paul moved on to Vicarage Road , the home of which club?

STEVE FINNAN

641. Steve is the only footballer in the world to have done what?

642. In 1993 Steve began his career with which non-League 'United' based in the London Borough of Bexley?

643. Following on from the previous question, Steve moved to The Blues from this club in what year?

644. In 1996 The Blues sent Steve out on loan to which 'County', the club that he signed for later that year when he left St Andrew's?

645. In 1998 Steve moved on to which London side?

646. Following on from the previous question, what European trophy did Steve win with this team?

647. Steve spent five years with the club in Question 645 before packing his bags for which Lancashire team?

648. Against which Euro 2004 winners did Steve make his debut for the Republic of Ireland in 2000?

649. Following on from the previous question, Steve was awarded his first cap in this game after replacing which injured right back, who joined The Blues in February 2009?

650. Name the Spanish outfit that Steve joined on transfer deadline day, 1 September 2008.

THE BLUES V. LONDON CLUBS

651. What is The Blues' biggest win over Arsenal, achieved at St Andrew's on 8 December 1906 - 5-1, 6-2 or 8-3?

652. The Blues beat which London side 4-0 at St Andrew's in season 1973/74 to record their best ever victory over them?

653. What is The Blues' biggest win over Chelsea, achieved at St Andrew's on 25 October 1930 - 4-0, 6-2 or 7-3?

654. What is the highest aggregate number of goals scored in a Birmingham City versus Tottenham Hotspur game?

655. Following on from the previous question, what was the score in this game, which took place at White Hart Lane on 18 September 1957 in the First Division?

656. Up to and including the 2008/09 season, which London club did The Blues meet for the last time in the League Cup in season 2002/03, beating them 3-2 away?

657. Birmingham City and Chelsea met at St Andrew's for a First Division game on New Year's Eve 1978 and the fan were treated to nine goals, but what was the score?

658. In season 1960/61 which team, who went on to become the first English side in the 20th century to win the coveted Double that season, beat The Blues home (6-0) and away (3-2) in the First Division?

659. What is the highest aggregate number of goals scored in a Birmingham City versus West Ham United game?

660. Following on from the previous question, what was the score of the game, which took place at Upton Park on 8 October 1961?

APPEARANCES - 2

Match up the player with the number of competitive appearances he made for the club in his career

661.	Frank Worthington	2
662.	Mark Ward	31
663.	Mick Harford	55 (8)
664.	Jimmy Calderwood	109
665.	Ian Atkins	64
666.	Trevor Aylott	114
667.	John Connolly	26
668.	Paul Cooper	84 (4)
669.	Tony Coton	114 (3)
670.	Roy McDonough	147 (12)

PETER NDLOVU

671. How many League goals did Peter score in his Birmingham City career – 23, 33 or 43?

672. In which year was Peter born – 1973, 1975 or 1977?

673. From which club did Peter sign in 1997 to join the playing staff at St Andrew's?

674. Against which team did Peter score a brace for The Blues in a 3-1 away League win during November 1998?

675. Which manager signed Peter for The Blues?

676. In what position did Peter play during his playing days?

677. Against which team did Peter score a brace for The Blues in a 3-1 away League win during February 1998?

678. Against which team did Peter score on his Blues debut in a 2-0 home League win during August 1997?

679. True or false: Peter is the all-time leading scorer for the Zimbabwean national team with 38 international goals?

680. For which club did Peter sign in 2001 when he left St Andrew's?

POSITIONS IN THE LEAGUE – 3

Match up the season with Birmingham City's finishing position in the League

681.	1946/1947	12th in Division 1
682.	1948/1949	9th in Division 1
683.	1950/1951	22nd in Division 1
684.	1952/1953	17th in Division 1
685.	1954/1955	18th in Division 1
686.	1956/1957	4th in Division 2
687.	1958/1959	20th in Division 1
688.	1960/1961	3rd in Division 2
689.	1962/1963	1st in Division 2
690.	1964/1965	6th in Division 2

CAPS FOR MY COUNTRY

Match up the player with the number of caps
he won for his country

691.	Gil Merrick	10 with the Republic of Ireland
692.	Michael Johnson	15 with Wales
693.	Malcolm Page	17 with England
694.	Kenny Cunningham	17 with Zimbabwe
695.	Jeff Hall	16 with Wales
696.	John Roberts	1 with Scotland
697.	Johnny Crosbie	28 with Wales
698.	Dave Langan	11 with Jamaica
699.	Peter Ndlovu	23 with England
700.	Terry Hennessey	32 with the Republic of Ireland

BIRMINGHAM CITY
V. ASTON VILLA - 2

701. Up to the end of the 2008/09 season, in what season did The Blues last record a derby win over their fiercest rivals?

702. What is the heaviest defeat suffered by the club in a derby game with Aston Villa - 6-2, 7-3 or 9-1?

703. From the first League meeting in 1879 up until the end of season 2008/09 there have been 124 competitive first-class meetings between the two teams, but how many of these did The Blues win – 34, 39 or 43?

704. In the derby at Villa Park in March 2003 Aston Villa's Dion Dublin was sent off for headbutting which Birmingham player?

705. Following on from the previous question, Villa's Joey Gudjonsson was also given his marching orders following a two-footed tackle on which Blues defender?

706. Villa holds the record for the biggest winning margin in a derby game involving the two teams. Give either the score or by how many goals Villa won the game at Villa Park on 12 October 1988?

707. Who was the last player to score a goal for The Blues in a derby game between the two sides, in a 5-1 loss at Villa Park on 20 April 2008?

708. Name the director of Birmingham City in the late 1960s, who formed part of a consortium that took over Aston Villa in 1968.

709. In 2006 who was the last player to move directly from Birmingham City to Aston Villa?

710. Who was the last manager to leave one of the clubs for the other?

MARTIN O'CONNOR

711. Martin began his career with which 'Rovers' in 1991?

712. In 1992 Martin signed for which London outfit?

713. Following on from the previous question, Martin was sent on loan by this team to which Midlands club, subsequently signing for them in 1994?

714. Can you recall the year in which Martin arrived at St Andrew's?

715. Name the 'Posh' team that Martin left to join The Blues.

716. In what year did Martin leave Birmingham City?

717. When Martin left The Blues he re-joined which former club?

718. To the nearest 30, how many League games did Martin play for Birmingham City?

719. How many League goals did Martin score for The Blues – 16, 21 or 26?

720. Although he was born in Walsall, Martin was called up to play for which 'Islands' team at international level?

ALAN CURBISHLEY

721. At which London club did Alan begin his professional playing career in 1975?

722. Following on from the previous question, Alan made his debut for this team in March 1975, just two months before they won which silverware?

723. During his playing days Alan was given what nickname by teammate Pat Holland, also the surname of a fictional character in the popular comic The Beano?

724. In what year in the 1970s did Alan sign for The Blues?

725. To the nearest £25,000, how much did Birmingham pay for Alan's services?

726. Alan made his debut for The Blues in a 4-3 loss to the team that the club in Question 721 beat to win the trophy in Question 722. Name the team.

727. How many League appearances did Alan make for Birmingham – 128, 138 or 148?

728. In what year did Alan leave St Andrew's?

729. Name the team that Alan joined when he left The Blues.

730. Can you name the club that gave Alan his first taste of management?

JOE GALLAGHER

731.   In what year in the 1970s did Joe begin his
       professional playing career with Birmingham City?

732.   Joe was only 18 years old when he made his debut for
       The Blues, in a 1-0 away defeat against which London
       club?

733.   Joe helped The Blues back to Division 1 in which
       season, following relegation the previous season?

734.   Can you name the year in which Joe left St Andrew's?

735.   Joe moved from The Blues to which Midlands outfit?

736.   To the nearest 50, how many appearances did Joe
       make for The Blues?

737.   How much did the team in Question 735 pay for Joe's
       services - £350,000, £450,000 or £550,000?

738.   In 1983 Joe moved to The Boleyn Ground to play for
       which London side?

739.   Following on from the previous question, when Joe left
       this club he moved to which Lancashire team, who
       reached the quarter-finals of the European Cup in
       season 1960/61?

740.   Following on again, just two months after his arrival at
       this club he was sent on loan to which Yorkshire
       'Town'?

FA CUP WINNERS & LOSERS

741. Which 2008 FA Cup winners knocked The Blues out of the 1975/76 competition, winning a 3rd round replay 1-0 at St Andrew's?

742. Which 1983/84 runners-up knocked Birmingham City out en route to Wembley this season?

743. Which Midlands rivals, winners of the FA Cup in 1960 for the fourth time in their history, eliminated The Blues from the 1995/96 FA Cup?

744. A 'University' team put Small Heath (later renamed Birmingham City) out of the 1879/80 FA Cup and then lost to Clapham Rovers in the final. Name them.

745. Can you name the first winners of the FA Cup after World War II who beat The Blues (then Small Heath) in round 1 of the 1902/03 competition?

746. In 1927/28 which club, who went on to win more FA Cups in history than any other side, eliminated Birmingham City from the Cup?

747. To the nearest 50, how many FA Cup games have The Blues played since their first participation in season 1878/79 up until season 2008/09?

748. Following on from the previous question and to the nearest 30, how many of these FA Cup ties did The Blues win?

749. Name the Yorkshire 'Town', FA Cup winners in 1922 for the only time in their history, which knocked The Blues out of the FA Cup in season 2007/08.

750. Which seven-times FA Cup winners (up to the end of the 2008/09 season) were the first club to defeat The Blues (then Small Heath) in an FA Cup tie in the 20th century?

JON McCARTHY

751.   What is Jon's middle name – Daniel, Damien or David?

752.   From which club did Jon sign to join The Blues in 1997?

753.   How many caps did Jon win for Northern Ireland in his career – 19, 29 or 39?

754.   In which year was Jon born in Middlesbrough – 1969, 1970 or 1971?

755.   For which team did Jon play between 1990 and 1995?

756.   Against which team did Jon make his Blues debut during September 1997 in a 1-0 home League defeat?

757.   Against which East Anglian team did Jon score his first goal for The Blues, in the 83rd minute of a 1-0 away League win on Boxing Day 1997?

758.   How many League goals did Jon score for Birmingham in his career – 8, 12 or 16?

759.   Which Blues manager signed Jon for the club?

760.   Against which East Anglian team did Jon score the only goal, in the 11th minute of a 1-0 away League win during August 1999?

ST ANDREW'S - 1

761. St Andrew's has been the home of Birmingham City ever since it first opened its doors, in what year during the early 20th century?

762. To the nearest 10,000, what is the record attendance for St Andrew's?

763. Following on from the previous question, the record crowd turned up to see The Blues play in an FA Cup tie which resulted in a 2-2 draw during 1939 against The Toffees, who are better known by what name?

764. In what year was the ground completely renovated to make it an all-seater stadium and thereby comply with The Taylor Report?

765. In which 'Street' did The Blues play their home games prior to moving to St Andrew's?

766. The site where St Andrew's was constructed housed what prior to the ground being built for the club?

767. St Andrew's was officially opened on Boxing Day in the year in Question 761. Name The Blues' north-east opponents that day.

768. Birmingham City's first ever win at St Andrew's was a 3-0 victory over the first club to achieve the domestic Double in English football. Name them.

769. St Andrew's was chosen by the Football Association to host an FA Cup semi-final in 1907. Name 'The Owls' who beat Woolwich Arsenal 3-1 and went on to win the FA Cup.

770. To help with Britain's war effort what did the club allow the ground to be used for during World War II?

MIXED BAG – 6

771. During their successful promotion-winning season in 1984/85 The Blues claimed a victory home and away in the League over 'The Eagles', who are better known by what name?

772. Which Blues legend was born in a south-western part of the city of Glasgow whose name is the same as his surname?

773. Name the two clubs that former Blue Alan Curbishley both played for and managed.

774. To the nearest £25,000, how much did Birmingham City receive from Manchester City for Robert Hopkins in 1986?

775. Name the future Blues striker who was not selected for the 1998 World Cup finals in France as England manager Glenn Hoddle claimed he needed six or seven chances to score one goal.

776. Which player did The Blues sign for £2.5 million in August 2007 and was later described by Blues chairman, David Sullivan, as a "rubbish signing"?

777. Which Blues player is the only outfield player to have played every minute of every game for his club in the Premier League in season 2007/08?

778. Which Blues midfielder was nicknamed 'Nasty' by the fans because of his fiery temperament on the pitch?

779. In season 2007/08 a Blues midfielder was ranked by Sky Sports Opta statistics as the most accurate taker of a direct free kick in the Premiership. Name him.

780. Name any four of the five Republic of Ireland players who played for The Blues (including any on loan to or from The Blues) in season 2008/09.

THEY WORE THE SHIRT – 1

781. Which 1963 League Cup winner left The Blues in 1965 to return to his former club Glasgow Celtic and won a European Cup winners' medal with the Scottish giants in 1967?

782. Who is the only player to have played 10 or more League games for the club and whose surname begins with the letter 'Z'?

783. Can you name the striker that The Blues took on loan from Portsmouth on 21 March 2007?

784. On leaving The Blues in 1976 which legendary Blues captain moved to the USA and played for the Portland Timbers and the Minnesota Kicks?

785. The Blues bought a Welsh international goalkeeper from Leeds United in 1973 who was a good shot stopper but also prone to the odd calamitous blunder. Name him.

786. Which ex-Blues defender (1996-99) is the only player to have won an FA Cup winners' medal with both Merseyside clubs, Everton and Liverpool?

787. Name the former Birmingham City centre half who was the first English player to captain a Double-winning team in the 20th century.

788. Which striker played for The Blues, one of his 15 League clubs, between 1994 and 1996, and in season 2008/09 could be found as a guest on the BBC's Football Focus?

789. Who played for The Blues from 1947 to 1948 and had a son of the same name who in 1966 won a World Cup winners' medal as a Blackpool player?

790. Who joined The Blues from Nottingham Forest in 1979, having been dropped for the 1979 European Cup final, and scored a famous goal for Scotland in the 1978 World Cup final to put the Scots 3-1 up versus Holland?

DARREN PURSE

791. From which club did The Blues sign Darren in 1998?

792. In which year was Darren born – 1975, 1976 or 1977?

793. Against which East Anglian team did Darren score the Blues' winner, a 62nd-minute penalty, in a 2-1 League win during February 2001?

794. Against which team did Darren score his first Blues goal, in Birmingham's 2-0 League Cup 3rd round win during October 1999?

795. Against which team did Darren make his Blues debut in a 2-0 away win during February 1998?

796. How many League goals did Darren score in his Blues career – 9, 19 or 29?

797. Which Blues manager signed Darren for Birmingham City?

798. At which London club did Darren start his professional football career, leaving in July 1996 for Oxford United?

799. What is Darren's middle name – John, Joshua or James?

800. Which club did Darren join in 2004 when he left St Andrew's?

LEAGUE CUP

801. Including the 2008/09 competition and to the nearest 50, how many League Cup games have The Blues played?

802. Name 'The Pilgrims' who were the first team to knock Birmingham City out of the League Cup.

803. The 1979 runners-up to Nottingham Forest, FA Cup winners during the 1970s, put The Blues out of the League Cup in 2008/09. Name them.

804. Which 1993/94 League Cup winners beat Manchester United in the final, stopping them from winning all three domestic trophies that season, and beat The Blues in an earlier round of the competition?

805. Name the 'Pirates' who put The Blues out of the 1970/71 League Cup.

806. Including the 2008/09 competition, who were the last winners of a League Cup to eliminate The Blues from the League Cup, winning 3-0 at home in season 2007/08?

807. In seasons 1972/73 and 1976/77 a Lancashire outfit eliminated Birmingham City from the League Cup. Name them.

808. The first ever winners of the League Cup at Wembley in 1966/67 put Birmingham City out of the League Cup in the semi-finals that season. Who are they?

809. Which Yorkshire side was the first team The Blues beat in the competition?

810. In 1968/69 which 'Town' caused a major upset by defeating Arsenal 3-1 in the League Cup final and in season 1961/62 put The Blues out of the competition?

CAMERON JEROME

811. In which year was Cameron born in Huddersfield – 1984, 1985 or 1986?

812. What squad number did Cameron wear for The Blues during the 2008/09 season?

813. From which Welsh side did Cameron sign to join The Blues in 2006?

814. Which Blues manager signed Cameron for the club?

815. How many England Under-21 caps has Cameron won for his country?

816. Against which club did Cameron make his Blues League debut, in a 2-1 home win during August 2006?

817. True or false: Cameron was sent off on his Blues League debut?

818. How many League goals did Cameron score for The Blues during his first season at St Andrew's, 2006/07?

819. Against which team did Cameron score Birmingham's only goal after 73 minutes in a 1-0 Championship away win during April 2009?

820. Against which team did Cameron score a brace for The Blues, in a 4-1 home win on the final day of the 2007/08 season?

SQUAD NUMBERS 2008/2009 – 2

*Match up the player with the squad number
he wore during the season*

821.	Robin Shroot	16
822.	David Murphy	26
823.	Maik Taylor	31
824.	Mehdi Nafti	3
825.	Kevin Phillips	32
826.	Franck Queudrue	22
827.	Damien Johnson	20
828.	Mitchell McPike	9
829.	Lee Carsley	1
830.	James McFadden	12

DELE ADEBOLA

831. In which year was Dele born –1974, 1975 or 1976?

832. In what position does Dele play?

833. In what year did Dele sign for The Blues?

834. Dele scored his first Blues League goal against his former club, opening the scoring after 42 minutes in a 2-0 away win. Who were the opponents?

835. How many League goals did Dele score in his Birmingham City career – 19, 29 or 39?

836. Against which London team did Dele score a brace for The Blues in a 3-1 away win in the League Cup 3rd round during October 2000?

837. True or false: Dele scored in The Blues' first five competitive matches of the 1998/99 season during August 1998?

838. Against which team did Dele make his Blues debut, in a 1-1 home draw?

839. What is Dele's real first name?

840. For which club did Dele sign in 2008?

WHERE DID THEY COME FROM? – 2

Match up the player with the team he left to join Birmingham City

841.	Curtis Woodhouse	Aston Villa
842.	Gary Rowett	West Ham United
843.	Anders Limpar	Celtic
844.	Kenny Brown	Exeter City
845.	George Parris	Middlesbrough
846.	Kevin Miller	Leicester City
847.	Liam Ridgewell	Sheffield United
848.	Olivier Tebily	Everton
849.	Steve Vickers	West Ham United
850.	Robbie Savage	Derby County

MIXED BAG - 7

851. The Blues have played seven clubs that have been in the Premier League every season since its inception in 1992/93. Name any five.

852. In their first season in the Premier League, 2002/03, The Blues lost home and away to a team that on 26 December 1999 became the first Premier League side to field an entirely foreign starting line-up. Name them.

853. Which goalkeeper joined The Blues from Barnsley in March 2003 to cover for the injured Nico Vacse and 7 minutes into his debut and only Premier League game for the club dropped the ball at his feet, allowing Robbie Keane to pounce and score for Tottenham Hotspur in their 2-1 home win?

854. Name the former Birmingham City striker who married Karren Brady, the managing director of the club, in 1995?

855. Which speedy winger did The Blues sign from Manchester United in 1993, who moved on to Wycombe Wanderers two years later?

856. Name the Blues player from 1961/62 whose surname is an occupation and also the original name of Coventry City when it was formed in 1883?

857. Name the only player with four 'z's' in his name to pull on a jersey for The Blues.

858. The son of a Dutch paratrooper joined The Blues in 1967 from Aston Villa, stayed for four seasons and then signed for Oldham Athletic. Name the former striker.

859. Which French international signed for The Blues on 29 June 2007 and moved on to Wigan Athletic on 16 July 2008, reuniting with his former boss at The Blues, Steve Bruce?

860. Name the 2009 UEFA Champions League winner who spent a month on loan to The Blues from West Ham United in season 1999/2000.

SECOND DIVISION RUNNERS-UP – 1971/1972

861. Name the Carrow Road outfit that won the Second Division title, a team that The Blues drew 2-2 away with and hammered 4-0 at St Andrew's.

862. Which team, with the same letter repeated four times in their single-word name, were promoted to the First Division along with Birmingham and the Champions?

863. The Blues were eliminated from the League Cup at the first hurdle when they went down 2-0 at Loftus Road to which opponents?

864. Which 1971/72 FA Cup winners, who defeated Cup holders Arsenal in the final, ended The Blues' dreams of Wembley by beating them 3-0 in the semi-finals?

865. Following on from the previous question, can you name the famous Yorkshire ground that hosted the semi-final?

866. The Blues' first win of the campaign was against which Northern 'Blues', in a 3-2 win at St Andrew's on 21 August 1971?

867. Name any two of the three clubs located in or close to London that were relegated to Division 3 at the end of the 1971/72 season.

868. Which manager guided The Blues back into the top flight of English football?

869. On 25 April 1972 The Blues beat which 'City' 2-0 at St Andrew's, a team that in season 2008/09 played top-flight English football for the first time in their history?

870. On the final day of the season The Blues recorded a 1-0 win in London at a 'Road' named after an Australian city. Name the team or the 'Road'.

BRYAN HUGHES

871. From which Welsh team did Bryan sign when he joined The Blues?

872. In what year did Bryan join Birmingham City?

873. Against which club did Bryan score a brace for The Blues in a 4-2 home League win during August 1999?

874. Against which team did Bryan score a brace in a 2-1 Blues win in the FA Cup 4th round win during January 1998?

875. Against which team did Bryan score a brace in a 7-0 away League win during January 1998?

876. Which Blues manager signed Bryan for the club?

877. Against which team did Bryan make his Blues debut in a 2-0 away defeat?

878. How many League goals did Bryan score in his Birmingham City career – 30, 34 or 38?

879. In which year was Bryan born – 1976, 1977 or 1978?

880. Which London club did Bryan join when he left St Andrew's in 2004?

MARTIN TAYLOR

881. What is Martin's nickname?

882. In which year was Martin born – 1979, 1980 or 1981?

883. From which club did Martin join The Blues in 2004?

884. What squad number did Martin wear for The Blues during 2008/09?

885. How much did Birmingham City pay for Martin?

886. Against which team did Martin score his only Blues goal of the 2008/09 season, in a 1-1 away draw during March 2009?

887. True or false: Martin won a full international cap for England during his career?

888. Against which team did Martin make his Blues debut in a 3-0 home win during February 2004?

889. Martin scored his first Blues League goal in only his second game for the club, the team's first goal against which club in a 3-1 home win during March 2004?

890. For which East Anglian club did Martin play on loan from The Blues during November and December 2007?

CHRISTMAS NO.1's – 2

891. The Blues finished in 3rd place in Division 2 in 1980 when John Lennon had the UK Christmas No. 1 with which song?

892. The Blues finished in 19th place in League Division 1 in 1993 when which group had the UK Christmas No. 1 with 'Babe'?

893. The Blues finished 10th in Division 1 when Slade had the UK Christmas No. 1 with 'Merry Xmas Everybody'. What was the year?

894. The Blues finished in 5th place in League Division 1 in 2001 when Robbie Williams and Nicole Kidman had the UK Christmas No. 1 with which song?

895. The Blues finished in 17th place in Division 1 in 1975 when which Queen song was the UK Christmas No. 1?

896. The Blues finished in 19th place in Division 2 when Cliff Richard had the UK Christmas No. 1 with 'Mistletoe & Wine'. What was the year?

897. The Blues were runners-up in Division 3 in 1992 when Whitney Houston had the UK Christmas No. 1 with which song?

898. The Blues finished in 15th place in League 1 in 1996 when which group, named after a Scottish town, had the UK Christmas No. 1 with 'Knockin' on Heaven's Door'?

899. The Blues finished in 19th place in Division 1 when Johnny Mathis had the UK Christmas No. 1 with 'When a Child is Born'. What was the year?

900. The Blues finished in 11th place in Division 1 in 1978 when which group had the UK Christmas No. 1 with 'Mary's Boy Child'?

ROBERT HOPKINS

901. At which Midlands club did Robert begin his playing career in 1979?

902. Following on from the previous question, what trophy did the young Robert win with this team in 1980?

903. In what year did Robert's first spell with Birmingham City begin?

904. In what season did Robert help The Blues to clinch the Second Division Championship?

905. To the nearest 50, how many games did Robert play for Birmingham?

906. What was Robert's nickname during his playing career?

907. Can you name the Blue, a future West Ham United manager, who formed part of the deal that saw Robert leave the club in Question 901 while the Blue moved in the opposite direction?

908. Name the non-League club that Robert both scored against and scored an own goal for in The Blues FA Cup defeat to this team in 1986.

909. What 'City' did Robert join when he left The Blues in 1986?

910. From which team did Robert move to join Birmingham for his second spell?

THEY WORE THE SHIRT – 2

911. Which Blues striker joined Everton in 1987 and scored a goal for them to prevent Liverpool from setting a new record of 30 games unbeaten from the start of a season?

912. Which Blues winger was denied his first cap for Scotland in April 1956 because the game came just three days before Birmingham's appearance in the FA Cup final?

913. Which ex-Blues goalkeeper went on to win an FA Cup winners' medal in 1978 and a UEFA Cup winners' medal in 1981 after he left St Andrew's?

914. In season 2005/06 The Blues took a player on loan who when he played for Newcastle United in season 2008/09 became one of only four players to have played in every season of the Premier League from 1992/93 to 2008/09. Name him.

915. Name the shortest player ever to have played in the Premier League, and who played for The Blues in season 1994/95.

916. Which former Blues centre forward at the time of his retirement from playing in 1974 held the British record for the highest combined transfer fee?

917. Which English-Italian began his career at York City in 1985, was at St Andrew's in 1996, and had an 18-year football career in which he played for 12 different clubs?

918. In season 1983/84 which Blues forward won a European Cup winners' medal in 1980/81 with his previous club Liverpool as a non-playing substitute in the final?

919. Which 1978-81 Blue missed a last-minute penalty for Sheffield United in the last match of the 1980/81 season against Walsall at Bramall Lane in the old Division 3?

920. Who won a First Division Championship winners' medal with Derby County in 1974/75, was on loan to The Blues in 1978 and was the first English-born captain of the Scotland national team?

ANDREW JOHNSON

921.   How many England caps has Andrew won in his career?

922.   Which London team did Andrew join when he left St Andrew's in 2002?

923.   Against which team did Andrew score a brace, his last goals for the club, in a 3-2 home defeat during September 2001?

924.   How many League goals did Andrew score for The Blues during the 2001/02 season?

925.   Against which club did Andrew score a brace for The Blues in a 4-3 League Cup 2nd round, 1st leg win during September 2000?

926.   Against which club did Andrew score Birmingham's only goal in a 1-1 home draw during September 1999?

927.   Which Blues manager gave Andrew his debut for the club?

928.   How many League goals did Andrew score for The Blues in his career – 8, 18 or 28?

929.   In which year was Andrew born in Bedford – 1981, 1982 or 1983?

930.   Which London club did Andrew join in 2008 from Everton?

ST ANDREW'S - 2

931. On 16 September 1907 Birmingham lost at St Andrew's for the first time, in a 1-0 defeat to 'The Shakers', who are better known by what name?

932. What happened to St Andrew's in 1941, which forced the club to play home games at a neutral venue for a while?

933. Who were the opponents when the highest attendance for a League game at St Andrew's, 60,250, was set on 23 November 1935?

934. Including the 2008/09 competition, how many FA Cup semi-finals (excluding replays) have been played at St Andrew's?

935. Name any year in which St Andrew's has hosted the FA Vase final.

936. In what year during the late 1980s did St Andrew's host the play-off final replay to decide which club would be promoted to the First Division?

937. Following on from the previous question, name either of the two teams involved.

938. Can you name the athletics club that trained at St Andrew's until the 1920s?

939. Which rugby union tourists from the southern hemisphere beat a Midland Counties XV by 16 points to 5 on a muddy St Andrew's pitch in 1960?

940. The record attendance since St Andrew's was converted to an all-seater stadium is 29,588, in a Premier League game on 22 November 2003 against which London visitors resulting in a 3-0 Blues defeat?

WHERE DID THEY GO? – 2

*Match up the player with the team he joined
on leaving Birmingham City*

941.	Mikael Forssell	Stoke City
942.	Stephen Clemence	Crystal Palace
943.	Paul Peschisolido	Sunderland
944.	Vince Overson	Leicester City
945.	Jamie Clapham	Leicester City
946.	Chris Sutton	Wolves
947.	Bruno N'Gotty	Hannover
948.	Kenny Cunningham	Leicester City
949.	Neil Danns	Stoke City
950.	D.J. Campbell	Aston Villa

KEVIN PHILLIPS

951. In which year was Kevin born – 1971, 1972 or 1973?

952. From which team did Kevin join The Blues on a free transfer in July 2008?

953. Which manager signed Kevin for The Blues?

954. What is Kevin's nickname?

955. How many full international caps did Kevin win for England in his career?

956. What squad number was Kevin given when he joined The Blues?

957. Against which team did Kevin score his Birmingham debut goal, in a 1-0 home win during August 2008?

958. Against which team did Kevin score a brace for The Blues in a 3-2 away win in the Championship during November 2008?

959. How many League goals did Kevin score for The Blues during 2008/09 – 14, 16 or 18?

960. For which team did Kevin play between 1997 and 2003?

TREVOR FRANCIS - 3

961. Name the Italian team that Trevor played for between 1985 and 1987.

962. With which club did Trevor win the Scottish League Cup in 1987?

963. Which London club did Trevor join in 1987, taking over as their manager in November 1988?

964. Following on from the previous question, which ex-Blues boss did Trevor replace?

965. Which Yorkshire club did Trevor manage from 1991 to 1994?

966. Following on from the previous question, Trevor opted not to sign which legendary Manchester United striker when he was on trial at this club?

967. In what year did Trevor return to his spiritual home, St Andrew's, as boss of Birmingham City?

968. Trevor led The Blues to which final in season 2000/01?

969. Following on from the previous question, Trevor left St Andrew's shortly after losing this final in a dramatic penalty shootout against which team?

970. Trevor managed which London club from 2001 to 2003, who beat the team in Question 969 away in an FA Cup 4th round replay in February 2003?

WHAT'S IN A NAME?

971. Name the side that The Blues have met in every season they have played in the Premier League and which began life as St Domingo FC in 1878.

972. Which defender joined The Blues on loan from Derby County in 2001/02 and shares the same first name as a Swedish player who won the Men's Singles Tennis Championship?

973. The Blues met which team in the Premiership in season 2007/08 that was founded in 1880 as St Marks (West Gorton) by Anna Connell and two wardens of St Mark's Church?

974. Which 'Charlie' played for The Blues in season 1938/39 and shares his surname with the first name of a London football ground passed by the University Boat Race each year?

975. Name the team that The Blues have met in every season they have played in the Premier League and that was founded as Dial Square in 1886.

976. Which player won promotion to the First Division with The Blues at the end of season 1902/03 and shares his surname with something you can find in every pub in the UK?

977. In season 2007/08 The Blues twice met a Lancashire club in the Premier League that was founded as Christ Church FC in 1874 by Thomas Ogden, the schoolmaster at Christ Church?

978. Which 1949-50 Birmingham City player shares his sur name with both an Arab country in south-west Asia and a Page 3 model?

979. Which Welsh legend, who shares his surname with a famous Cognac, was a key player in the 1963/64 Birmingham City side that narrowly avoided relegation to Division 2?

980. Name the centre half who played for The Blues (then Small Heath) from 1888 to 1895 and Manchester United (then Newton Heath) from 1886 to 1887 and whose first name is the surname of a famous Roman Emperor?

STAN LAZARIDIS

981. In which year was Stan born – 1970, 1971 or 1972?

982. From which London club did The Blues sign Stan in 1999?

983. How many full international caps did Stan win for Australia?

984. Where on the pitch did Stan play - on the left side, on the right side or in the middle?

985. How many League goals did Stan score in his Birmingham City career?

986. Against which team did Stan make his Blues League debut, in a 2-2 home draw during August 1999?

987. True or false: following on from the previous question, Stan scored on his League debut for The Blues?

988. Which Blues manager signed Stan for the club and gave him his debut?

989. Against which Yorkshire club did Stan score Birmingham's winner in a 3-2 away win during January 2001?

990. Stan scored against which two teams during Birmingham's Premier League season 2003/04, the first in a 2-0 home win and the second in a 3-0 home win?

SECOND DIVISION RUNNERS-UP – 1984/1985

991. The Blues finished as runners-up to which Champions, a team that won promotion to Division 1 less than a quarter of a century after they were elected to the Football League?

992. Birmingham won 1-0 on the opening day of the season at Boundary Park, the home of which Lancashire side?

993. On 19 March 1985 The Blues drew 0-0 with which 'City', who along with Birmingham won promotion to Division 1 at the end of the season?

994. The last team to beat Birmingham during the season were 'The Mariners', beating The Blues 1-0 away, who are better known by what name?

995. During their successful promotion-winning campaign The Blues beat the First Division winners of 1954, 1958 and 1959 home and away. Name this famous Midlands side, which finished bottom of the League.

996. The Blues defeated home and away in the League a team that can proudly boast to be the oldest professional League club in the world. Who are they?

997. Which First Division 'Canaries' knocked The Blues out of the FA Cup and went on to win the League Cup in season 1984/85?

998. Name the Blues manager who guided the club to promotion to the top flight of English football.

999. Which Midlands rivals eliminated The Blues from the League Cup, in a 3-1 away defeat after a 0-0 draw at St Andrew's?

1000. On the last day of the season The Blues had a 1-0 win at St Andrew's against a team that won the Inter-Cities Fairs Cup (now the UEFA Cup) in 1968 and 1971. Name them.

ANSWERS

CLUB HISTORY & RECORDS

1. *1875*
2. *True: they were from the Holy Church in Bordesley Green*
3. *6th*
4. *Gil Merrick*
5. *1931 and 1956*
6. *Inter-Cities Fairs Cup*
7. *Small Heath Alliance (1875-88), Small Heath (1888-1905) and Birmingham (1905-45)*
8. *Emile Heskey*
9. *Joe Bradford*
10. *The Blues*

LEAGUE CUP RUNNERS-UP - 2001

11. *Liverpool*
12. *Darren Purse*
13. *Millennium Stadium, Cardiff*
14. *Trevor Francis*
15. *David Elleray*
16. *Ipswich Town*
17. *Michael Johnson*
18. *Southend United*
19. *Tottenham Hotspur*
20. *Dele Adebola*

MAIK TAYLOR

21. *Fulham*
22. *Stefan*
23. *Northern Ireland*
24. *Germany*
25. *Steve Bruce*
26. *1971*
27. *Farnborough Town*

28. False
29. £1.5 million
30. Goalkeeper

SQUAD NUMBERS 2008/2009 - 1

31.	Cameron Jerome	10
32.	Colin Doyle	13
33.	Martin Taylor	5
34.	Liam Ridgewell	6
35.	Jordon Mutch	17
36.	Radhi Jaidi	15
37.	Gary McSheffrey	11
38.	Sebastian Larsson	7
39.	Stuart Parnaby	21
40.	Marcus Bent	23

THE CHAMPIONSHIP RUNNERS-UP – 2006/2007

41. Steve Bruce
42. Sunderland
43. 26
44. True: won 5 and drew 1
45. Nicklas Bendtner
46. D.J. Campbell
47. Gary McSheffrey
48. Maik Taylor (27) and Colin Doyle (19)
49. Cameron Jerome
50. Derby County and Coventry City

SEBASTIAN LARSSON

51. 1985
52. Arsenal
53. Steve Bruce
54. Crystal Palace

55.   4

56.   Norwich City

57.   True

58.   6

59.   Colchester United

60.   Sweden

MANAGERS

61.	Steve Bruce	2001
62.	Lou Macari	1991
63.	Ron Saunders	1982
64.	Terry Cooper	1991
65.	Dave Mackay	1989
66.	Alex McLeish	2007
67.	John Bond	1986
68.	Barry Fry	1993
69.	Garry Pendrey	1987
70.	Trevor Francis	1996

TREVOR FRANCIS - 1

71.   1970 (5 September)

72.   16

73.   Cardiff City

74.   1979

75.   Nottingham Forest

76.   £999,999 (Brian Clough wanted to ensure that this milestone transfer fee did not go to the player's head, although when taxes were added the total fee was in excess of £1.1m)

77.   15

78.   Queens Park Rangers (In the game he glided in from the wing and past four defenders despite being turned back towards his own goal several times before unleashing an

unstoppable 25-yard screamer into the goal)

79.   **1977 (in a 2-0 loss to Holland)**

80.   **Don Revie**

THE BLUES IN EUROPE

81.   **1955/56**

82.   **The Inter-Cities Fairs Cup**

83.   **Zagreb**

84.   **Eddy Brown**

85.   **Inter Milan**

86.   **Bryan Orritt**

87.   **Winners**

88.   **3 (1955-58)**

89.   **Semi-finals**

90.   **FC Barcelona**

MALCOLM PAGE

91.   **Edward**

92.   **17**

93.   **391: 382 (9)**

94.   **Division 2 promotion, 1971/72**

95.   **Huddersfield Town**

96.   **1981**

97.   **Oxford United**

98.   **10**

99.   **Wales**

100.   **1947**

DIVISION 3 RUNNERS-UP – 1991/1992

101.   **Terry Cooper**

102.   **True: they lost to Preston North End and Wigan Athletic (April 1992) and Stockport County (May 1992)**

103.   **15**

104. **Kevin Drinkell**

105. **Simon Sturridge**

106. **True: three League goals was their highest number**

107. **Ian Rodgerson**

108. **12,399**

109. **Nigel Glenhorn**

110. **True: beating Bury, Fulham and Darlington (August 1991) and Hull City (September 1991)**

FREDDIE GOODWIN

111. **Manchester United**

112. **Matt Busby (later Sir Matt Busby and the famous 'Busby Babes')**

113. **First Division Championship winners' medal**

114. **Leeds United**

115. **£10,000**

116. **John Charles**

117. **Scunthorpe United**

118. **1970**

119. **Brighton & Hove Albion**

120. **Minnesota Kicks**

MIKAEL FORSSELL

121. **Finland**

122. **Steve Bruce**

123. **17**

124. **1981**

125. **£3 million**

126. **Scunthorpe United**

127. **March (2004)**

128. **Tottenham Hotspur**

129. **Sunderland**

130. **Chelsea**

NATIONALITIES

131.	Colin Doyle	Irish
132.	Stephen Carr	Irish
133.	Kevin Phillips	English
134.	Sebastian Larsson	Swedish
135.	James McFadden	Scottish
136.	Trevor Francis	English
137.	Franck Queudrue	French
138.	Malcolm Page	Welsh
139.	Michael Johnson	Jamaican
140.	Frank Mitchell	Australian

WHO AM I?

141. Andy Cole (he made his debut in 1995 v. Uruguay under Terry Venables, then played v. Italy under Glenn Hoddle in 1997, made his third appearance v. France under caretaker manager Howard Wilkinson in 1999 and won his fourth cap v. Poland in 1999 under Kevin Keegan)

142. Ray Martin

143. Liam Ridgewell (he left Villa for The Blues at the start of the 2007/08 season)

144. Alex Govan

145. Joe Gallagher (Joe maintains that this was merely an excuse to cut costs following their bankruptcy in 1982)

146. Freddie Goodwin

147. Sir Alf Ramsey (England manager when they won the famous trophy in 1966)

148. Paul Devlin

149. Robert Hopkins

150. Alan Curbishley (manager of Charlton Athletic at the time)

DES BREMNER

151. George

152. Hibernian
153. 1989
154. Ron Saunders
155. Huddersfield Town
156. Sheffield United
157. Leeds United
158. Aston Villa
159. 1
160. 1971

WHERE DID THEY COME FROM? - 1

161.	Marcus Bent	Charlton Athletic
162.	James McFadden	Everton
163.	Barry Horne	Everton
164.	Martin Grainger	Brentford
165.	Gary Ablett	Everton
166.	Mario Melchiot	Chelsea
167.	Darren Anderton	Tottenham Hotspur
168.	Dwight Yorke	Blackburn Rovers
169.	David Murphy	Hibernian
170.	Lee Carsley	Everton

LEAGUE CUP WINNERS - 1963

171. Aston Villa
172. Aston Villa 4-0 Birmingham City
173. Doncaster Rovers
174. Manchester City
175. Gil Merrick
176. Kevin Leek
177. Jimmy Bloomfield (Bloomfield Park, home of Blackpool)
178. Bury
179. 0-0
180. 3-1

ALEX GOVAN

181.   Plymouth Argyle

182.   1953 (June)

183.   The RAF

184.   Bob Brocklebank

185.   £6,500

186.   1956/57

187.   The Second Division Championship in season 1954/55

188.   1958

189.   Portsmouth

190.   Harry Hooper

FOOTBALL LEAGUE TROPHY WINNERS - 1991

191.   Leyland DAF

192.   Walsall

193.   Lincoln City

194.   Swansea City

195.   Mansfield Town

196.   Cambridge United (3-1 at St Andrew's)

197.   Brentford

198.   Tranmere Rovers

199.   Wembley Stadium

200.   Lou Macari

MIXED BAG - 1

201.   2 (84 points to 82)

202.   1962

203.   Alex Govan

204.   Reach the FA Cup final without playing a home tie in an earlier round of the competition

205.   6th

206.   Des Bremner

207.   Charlton Athletic

208.   19
209.   **Officially open the ground**
210.   **Henry Cooper**

BARRY FRY

211.   *1993*
212.   *Trevor Francis*
213.   *Barnet*
214.   *Francis*
215.   *True: 1994/95*
216.   *Terry Cooper*
217.   *Inside forward*
218.   *1945*
219.   *Southend United*
220.   *1995/96*

ALEX McLEISH

221.   *1959*
222.   *Big Eck*
223.   *Central defender*
224.   *77*
225.   *Glasgow Rangers*
226.   *2007 (November)*
227.   *Tottenham Hotspur*
228.   *Blackburn Rovers*
229.   *2nd*
230.   *Scotland*

APPEARANCES - 1

231.	Gary Sprake	22
232.	Dennis Mortimer	37
233.	Dave Latchford	239
234.	Howard Kendall	134

235.	Ted Duckhouse	139
236.	Alan Curbishley	153 (2)
237.	Alan Buckley	25 (4)
238.	Steve Lynex	45 (21)
239.	Fred Harris	312
240.	Julian Dicks	95 (7)

BRIAN ROBERTS

241. False: he was a defender
242. 1955
243. Second Division runners-up medal in 1985
244. 1984
245. Coventry City
246. Ron Saunders
247. 187
248. Harry
249. True
250. Wolverhampton Wanderers

RON SAUNDERS

251. Jim Smith
252. 17th
253. Centre forward
254. True: he managed Aston Villa between 1974 and 1982
255. Manage three West Midlands clubs in succession
256. Second Division runners-up medal in 1985
257. West Bromwich Albion
258. 1932
259. False: he never played for Birmingham City
260. John Bond

MATTHEW UPSON

261. James

262. **Central defender**

263. **Arsenal**

264. **2**

265. **West Ham United**

266. **Newcastle United**

267. **Bolton Wanderers**

268. **Steve Bruce**

269. **Germany**

270. **Luton Town**

CHRISTMAS NO. 1's – 1

271. **'Earth Song'**

272. **Blue, featuring Elton John**

273. **2003**

274. **'Caravan of Love'**

275. **1991**

276. **Westlife**

277. **1979**

278. **'Ernie (the Fastest Milkman in the West)'**

279. **Jimmy Osmond**

280. **1970**

FOOTBALL LEAGUE TROPHY WINNERS - 1995

281. **Barry Fry**

282. **Auto Windscreens**

283. **Peterborough United**

284. **Walsall**

285. **Gillingham**

286. **Hereford United**

287. **Swansea City**

288. **Leyton Orient**

289. **Carlisle United**

290. **Birmingham City 1-0 Carlisle United**

2008/2009

291. **Sheffield United**
292. **Kevin Phillips**
293. **Southampton**
294. **Ipswich Town**
295. **Wycombe Wanderers**
296. **Cardiff City (FA Cup winners in 1927)**
297. **Blackpool (renamed in 1887)**
298. **Wolverhampton Wanderers**
299. **Lee Bowyer (on loan from West Ham United; 1-1 home draw with Cardiff City)**
300. **Nottingham Forest**

STEVE BRUCE

301. **Roger**
302. **Centre back**
303. **Sheffield United**
304. **Wigan Athletic and Crystal Palace**
305. **Wolverhampton Wanderers**
306. **True: via the play-off final against Norwich City, winning 4-2 on penalties**
307. **False: the nearest he came was winning one 'B' cap for England in 1987**
308. **Heading for Victory**
309. **Sweeper!, Defender! and Striker!**
310. **Wigan Athletic**

STEPHEN CLEMENCE

311. **Tottenham Hotspur**
312. **8**
313. **Ray Clemence**
314. **1978**
315. **True: in January 2003**

316. **Liverpool**

317. **Christophe Dugarry and Stan Lazaridis**

318. **Leicester City**

319. **Dream Team**

320. **Neal**

JEFF KENNA

321. **Jude**

322. **27**

323. **1970**

324. **Blackburn Rovers**

325. **2002**

326. **St Patrick's Athletic**

327. **3**

328. **Tottenham Hotspur**

329. **Sheffield Wednesday**

330. **Derby County**

POSITIONS IN THE LEAGUE – 1

331.	1991/1992	2nd in Division 3
332.	1992/1993	19th in Division 2
333.	1993/1994	22nd in Division 1
334.	1994/1995	1st in Division 2
335.	1995/1996	15th in Division 1
336.	1996/1997	10th in Division 1
337.	1997/1998	7th in Division 1
338.	1998/1999	4th in Division 1
339.	1999/2000	5th in Division 1
340.	2000/2001	5th in Division 1

DAMIEN JOHNSON

341. **Michael**

342. **Northern Ireland**

343. Blackburn Rovers

344. 22

345. Steve Bruce

346. Bradford City

347. Leeds United

348. Everton

349. 1978

350. 9

LIAM RIDGEWELL

351. 2007

352. 6

353. Steve Bruce

354. 8

355. Jamie Mackie

356. 1984

357. Matthew

358. £2 million

359. Ipswich Town

360. Wigan Athletic

MIXED BAG - 2

361. Manchester City

362. Wolverhampton Wanderers

363. Brighton & Hove Albion

364. 5

365. Burnley and Wolverhampton Wanderers

366. Dick Turpin

367. A penalty shootout to determine the winner of an FA Cup tie
      (from 1970-74 the losing FA Cup semi-finalists had a play-off
      for 3rd and 4th place in the competition and The Blues,
      losing semi-finalists in 1972, had to endure the penalty
      shootout following a 0-0 draw with the other losing semi-
      finalists)

368. **Stoke City**

369. **Robert Hopkins**

370. **Freddie Goodwin**

IAN BENNETT

371. **Queens Park Rangers**

372. **Newcastle United**

373. **1993**

374. **Peterborough United**

375. **Barry Fry**

376. **£325,000**

377. **Coventry City and Sheffield United**

378. **2005**

379. **Leeds United**

380. **Sheffield United**

JULIAN DICKS

381. **1985**

382. **The Terminator**

383. **1988**

384. **West Ham United**

385. **£300,000**

386. **Liverpool**

387. **Score a goal at the Kop end before it became an all-seater stand**

388. **David Burrows**

389. **West Ham United**

390. **Canvey Island**

WHERE DID THEY GO? - 1

391. **Jeff Kenna**   **Derby County**

392. **Geoff Horsfield**   **Wigan Athletic**

393. **Darren Purse**   **West Bromwich Albion**

394.	Jon McCarthy	Port Vale
395.	Paul Furlong	Queens Park Rangers
396.	Danny Sonner	Walsall
397.	Nick Forster	Reading
398.	Kevin Poole	Bolton Wanderers
399.	Graham Hyde	Bristol Rovers
400.	Tony Rees	Barnsley

JOHN GAYLE

401. He worked in a printers and on a building site
402. Bromsgrove Rovers
403. Wimbledon (they beat Liverpool 1-0 in the 1988 final)
404. 1990
405. £175,000
406. Coventry City
407. Burnley
408. Torquay United
409. Northampton Town
410. Moor Green (known as Solihull Moors since 2007)

DIVISION TWO CHAMPIONS – 1994/1995

411. 1
412. Brentford
413. Leyton Orient
414. Blackburn Rovers
415. Slough Town
416. Blackpool
417. Barry Fry
418. Huddersfield Town
419. Liverpool
420. It was the first time that five clubs had been relegated from any of the League's four divisions

GEOFF HORSFIELD

421.   1973

422.   Trevor Francis

423.   23

424.   5th

425.   West Bromwich Albion

426.   5

427.   Fulham

428.   League Cup runners-up medal in 2001 and First Division play-off winners medal in 2002

429.   Striker

430.   Malcolm

POSITIONS IN THE LEAGUE – 2

431.	1967/1968	4th in Division 2
432.	1969/1970	18th in Division 2
433.	1971/1972	2nd in Division 2
434.	1973/1974	19th in Division 1
435.	1975/1976	19th in Division 1
436.	1977/1978	11th in Division 1
437.	1979/1980	3rd in Division 2
438.	1981/1982	16th in Division 1
439.	1983/1984	20th in Division 1
440.	1985/1986	21st in Division 1

MIXED BAG - 3

441.   Radhi Ben Abdelmajid Jaïdi

442.   Germain 'Kemy' Agustien

443.   Lee Bowyer

444.   5

445.   John Bond

446.   Damien Johnson (Lee Carsley was acting captain)

447.   Crossroads

448. Carpenter
449. Ulises de la Cruz
450. The England national team (Sven-Goran Eriksson was stepping down after the 2006 World Cup finals)

PAUL TAIT
451. 1988
452. Auto Windscreens Trophy final (1995)
453. Aston Villa
454. 2
455. Millwall
456. Northampton Town
457. 1999
458. Oxford United
459. 170
460. Cyprus (or The Republic of Cyprus)

MIXED BAG – 4
461. Freddie Goodwin
462. Paul Devlin
463. Ulises de la Cruz (number 27 was previously worn by Krystian Pearce, who was out on loan for the season, and the Football League ruled that this number could not be reused)
464. Radhi Ben Abdelmajid Jaïdi (he captained the Tunisian national team)
465. Charlton Athletic
466. Franck Queudrue
467. Stephen Carr (Republic of Ireland)
468. Sebastian Larsson
469. Artur Krysiak
470. Arsenal

MICHAEL JOHNSON
471. 12

472. Jamaican
473. 12
474. Derby County
475. Magic
476. 3
477. Newcastle United
478. Owen
479. Barry Fry
480. Notts County

ALBERTO TARANTINI

481. Argentinean
482. Boca Juniors
483. Rabbit
484. A FIFA World Cup winners' medal with Argentina
485. 1978 (October)
486. £295,000
487. Jim Smith
488. Tottenham Hotspur
489. Brian Greenhoff
490. 1979

BIRMINGHAM CITY V. ASTON VILLA - 1

491. The Second City Derby
492. 1879
493. Small Heath (Birmingham City) 1-0 Aston Villa
494. It was the first time the two sides had met in a Football League game (Aston Villa won 2-1 in Division 1)
495. Aston Villa 3-0 Birmingham City (the game ended 3-3)
496. Birmingham City 4-0 Aston Villa
497. 2002/03
498. Aston Villa 0-2 Birmingham City and Birmingham City 3-0 Aston Villa

499.   124

500.   *It was the first derby that the club played as Birmingham City after changing their name from Small Heath (The Blues won 2-0 in Division 1)*

LEGENDS

501.   **Gil Merrick**

502.   **Ray Martin**

503.   **Ken Green**

504.   **Joe Bradford**

505.   **Ian Bennett**

506.   **Fred Harris**

507.   **Roy Warhurst**

508.   **Dennis Jennings**

509.   **Kenny Burns**

510.   **Alan Curbishley**

GOALSCORERS - 1

511.	Andy Kennedy	21
512.	Pat Van Den Hauwe	1
513.	Alan Ainscow	22
514.	Bob Hatton	73
515.	Roger Hynd	5
516.	Jack Mulraney	16
517.	George Parris	2
518.	David Rennie	4
519.	Steve Whitton	35
520.	Peter Withe	11

THE CHAMPIONSHIP – PLAY-OFF WINNERS – 2001/2002

521.   **Manchester City**

522.   **Nationwide (Nationwide Building Society)**

523.   **Millwall**

524. **Liverpool (The Blues lost 3-0 at Anfield in round 3)**

525. **Sheffield United**

526. **Millwall**

527. **Norwich City**

528. **0-0 (and 1-1 after extra time, with The Blues winning 4-2 on penalties)**

529. **Geoff Horsfield**

530. **16**

FORMER AWAY GROUNDS

531. **Manchester City**

532. **Leicester City**

533. **Sunderland**

534. **Middlesbrough**

535. **Wimbledon**

536. **Brighton & Hove Albion**

537. **Coventry City**

538. **Southampton**

539. **Reading**

540. **Derby County**

PAUL FURLONG

541. **Enfield (re-formed as Enfield 1893, the year being the date Enfield FC was founded)**

542. **Coventry City**

543. **1996**

544. **Chelsea**

545. **Crystal Palace**

546. **£1.5 million**

547. **Sheffield United (2002)**

548. **Queens Park Rangers**

549. **Luton Town**

550. **Barnet**

TREVOR FRANCIS - 2

551. 1980
552. Malmö FF
553. The Olympiastadion, Munich (home to Bayern Munich at the time)
554. John Robertson
555. Johan Cruyff
556. Wolverhampton Wanderers
557. Manchester City
558. John Bond (Blues manager 1986-87)
559. Sampdoria
560. The Coppa Italia

MIXED BAG – 5

561. Sheffield United
562. 1976
563. Alex Govan
564. 1955/56
565. Hameur Bouazza
566. Joe Gallagher
567. Carlo Yaír Costly Molina
568. Stephen Carr
569. Franck Queudrue
570. Djimi Traoré

HOWARD KENDALL

571. Preston North End
572. At the time he was the youngest player to appear in the FA Cup final in the 20th century
573. Everton
574. The Holy Trinity
575. 1974
576. 118

577. **Blackburn Rovers**

578. **Athletic Bilbao**

579. **Everton**

580. **Win one of Europe's major trophies (the European Cup Winners' Cup with Everton in 1985)**

BIRMINGHAM CITY V. WEST BROMWICH ALBION

581. **1885/86**

582. **The FA Cup**

583. **WBA 4-0 Small Heath**

584. **2006/07**

585. **WBA 1-1 Birmingham City**

586. **4 (Birmingham City 4-0, 18 December 2004, Premiership)**

587. **Birmingham City 1-7 WBA (18 April 1960, Division 1)**

588. **124**

589. **On their 10th encounter (WBA 0-1 Small Heath 1, 12 March 1904, FA Cup)**

590. **Damien Johnson**

GOALSCORERS - 2

591.	**Billy Wright**	**14**
592.	**Mark Sale**	**3**
593.	**Dai Richards**	**2**
594.	**Steve McGavin**	**7**
595.	**Martin Kuhl**	**6**
596.	**Robert Hopkins**	**33**
597.	**Nigel Gleghorn**	**42**
598.	**Barry Bridges**	**46**
599.	**Bert Murray**	**23**
600.	**Phil Sproson**	**1**

MARTIN GRAINGER

601. **Colchester United**

602. *25*

603. *1972*

604. *Brentford*

605. *Cheshunt Football Club*

606. *Robert*

607. *Left back*

608. *The fans' Player of the Year award*

609. *Stockport County*

610. *Oxford United*

CHRISTOPHE DUGARRY

611. *Bordeaux*

612. *1993*

613. *AC Milan*

614. *FC Barcelona*

615. *2003*

616. *Olympique Marseilles*

617. *A FIFA World Cup winners' medal with France*

618. *The 2000 European Championship*

619. *2004*

620. *Qatar Sports Club*

MICK HARFORD

621. *Lincoln City*

622. *Newcastle United*

623. *1982*

624. *£100,000*

625. *Bristol City*

626. *Luton Town*

627. *Chelsea*

628. *Wimbledon*

629. *Nottingham Forest*

630. *Luton Town*

PAUL DEVLIN

631. Notts County

632. 1996 (29th February 1996)

633. £250,000

634. 123

635. 32

636. 1998 (13th March 1998)

637. Sheffield United

638. Steve Bruce

639. 2004 (at the end of the 2003-04 season)

640. Watford

STEVE FINNAN

641. He is the only player to have played in the World Cup, Champions League, UEFA Cup, all four levels of English League football, the English Conference and Spain's La Liga

642. Welling United

643. 1993

644. Notts County

645. Fulham

646. The UEFA Intertoto Cup in 2002

647. Liverpool

648. Greece

649. Stephen Carr

650. Espanyol

THE BLUES V. LONDON CLUBS

651. 5-1

652. Queens Park Rangers

653. 6-2

654. 8

655. Tottenham Hotspur 7-1 Birmingham City

656. Leyton Orient

657. Birmingham City 4-5 Chelsea

658. Tottenham Hotspur

659. 7

660. West Ham United 4-3 Birmingham City

APPEARANCES - 2

661.	Frank Worthington	84 (4)
662.	Mark Ward	64
663.	Mick Harford	109
664.	Jimmy Calderwood	147 (12)
665.	Ian Atkins	114 (3)
666.	Trevor Aylott	31
667.	John Connolly	55 (8)
668.	Paul Cooper	26
669.	Tony Coton	114
670.	Roy McDonough	2

PETER NDLOVU

671. 23

672. 1973

673. Coventry City

674. West Bromwich Albion

675. Trevor Francis

676. Striker

677. Wolverhampton Wanderers

678. Stoke City

679. True

680. Sheffield United

POSITIONS IN THE LEAGUE – 3

681.	1946/1947	3rd in Division 2
682.	1948/1949	17th in Division 1
683.	1950/1951	4th in Division 2

684.	1952/1953	6th in Division 2
685.	1954/1955	1st in Division 2
686.	1956/1957	12th in Division 1
687.	1958/1959	9th in Division 1
688.	1960/1961	18th in Division 1
689.	1962/1963	20th in Division 1
690.	1964/1965	22nd in Division 1

CAPS FOR MY COUNTRY

691.	Gil Merrick	23 with England
692.	Michael Johnson	11 with Jamaica
693.	Malcolm Page	28 with Wales
694.	Kenny Cunningham	32 with the Republic of Ireland
695.	Jeff Hall	17 with England
696.	John Roberts	15 with Wales
697.	Johnny Crosbie	1 with Scotland
698.	Dave Langan	10 with the Republic of Ireland
699.	Peter Ndlovu	17 with Zimbabwe
700.	Terry Hennessey	16 with Wales

BIRMINGHAM CITY V. ASTON VILLA - 2

701. 2004/05 (The Blues won both Premier League games)

702. 7-3 (on 7 September 1895 at Villa Park when City were still Small Heath)

703. 39

704. Robbie Savage

705. Matthew Upson

706. Aston Villa 5-0 Birmingham City

707. Mikael Forssell

708. Doug Ellis

709. Chris Sutton

710. Ron Saunders (leaving Villa in 1982 to manage The Blues)

MARTIN O'CONNOR

711. **Bromsgrove Rovers**
712. **Crystal Palace**
713. **Walsall**
714. **1996**
715. **Peterborough United**
716. **2002**
717. **Walsall**
718. **186**
719. **16**
720. **The Cayman Islands**

ALAN CURBISHLEY

721. **West Ham United**
722. **The FA Cup**
723. **Whizz (Billy Whizz is a Beano character)**
724. **1979 (April)**
725. **£225,000**
726. **Fulham**
727. **128**
728. **1983**
729. **Aston Villa**
730. **Charlton Athletic**

JOE GALLAGHER

731. **1972**
732. **Arsenal**
733. **1979/80**
734. **1981**
735. **Wolverhampton Wanderers**
736. **335**
737. **£350,000**
738. **West Ham United (the Boleyn Ground is the official name for their home ground, but Upton Park is most commonly used)**

739. **Burnley**

740. **Halifax Town**

FA CUP WINNERS & LOSERS

741. **Portsmouth**

742. **Watford**

743. **Wolverhampton Wanderers**

744. **Oxford University**

745. **Derby County**

746. **Manchester United**

747. **296**

748. **125 (drew 58 and lost 113)**

749. **Huddersfield Town**

750. **Aston Villa (1900/01)**

JON McCARTHY

751. **David**

752. **Port Vale**

753. **19**

754. **1970**

755. **York City**

756. **Sunderland**

757. **Ipswich Town**

758. **8**

759. **Trevor Francis**

760. **Norwich City**

ST ANDREW'S - 1

761. **1906**

762. **67,341**

763. **Everton**

764. **1993**

765. **Muntz Street**

766. A brickworks
767. Middlesbrough (the First Division game ended 0-0)
768. Preston North End (Double winners in 1888/89) on 29 December 1906
769. Sheffield Wednesday
770. A rifle range for military training

MIXED BAG – 6

771. Crystal Palace
772. Alex Govan
773. Charlton Athletic and West Ham United
774. £130,000
775. Andy Cole
776. Franck Queudrue
777. Stephen Kelly
778. Mehdi Nafti
779. Alfe Inge Sebastian Larsson
780. Stephen Carr, Lee Carsley, Colin Doyle, Keith Fahey and Stephen Kelly

THEY WORE THE SHIRT - 1

781. Bertie Auld
782. Mauro Matías Zárate (14 League games while on loan in 2008)
783. Andy Cole (played 5 games and scored 1 goal)
784. Ray Martin
785. Gary Sprake
786. Gary Ablett (with Liverpool in 1989 and Everton in 1995)
787. Steve Bruce (with Manchester United, 1993/94)
788. Steve Claridge
789. Alan Ball
790. Archie Gemmill

DARREN PURSE

791. Oxford United
792. 1977
793. Norwich City
794. Newcastle United
795. Crewe Alexandra
796. 9
797. Trevor Francis
798. Leyton Orient
799. John
800. West Bromwich Albion

LEAGUE CUP

801. 176
802. Plymouth Argyle (in 1960/61)
803. Southampton
804. Aston Villa
805. Bristol Rovers
806. Blackburn Rovers (winners in 2001/02)
807. Blackpool
808. Queens Park Rangers
809. Bradford Park Avenue (in 1960/61)
810. Swindon Town

CAMERON JEROME

811. 1986
812. 10
813. Cardiff City
814. Steve Bruce
815. 10
816. Colchester
817. True: he came on as a substitute after 65 minutes and got sent off after 70 minutes

818.   7

819.   Watford

820.   Blackburn Rovers

SQUAD NUMBERS 2008/2009 - 2

821.   Robin Shroot   32

822.   David Murphy   3

823.   Maik Taylor   1

824.   Mehdi Nafti   12

825.   Kevin Phillips   9

826.   Franck Queudrue   20

827.   Damien Johnson   22

828.   Mitchell McPike   31

829.   Lee Carsley   26

830.   James McFadden   16

DELE ADEBOLA

831.   1975

832.   Striker

833.   1998

834.   Crewe Alexandra

835.   29

836.   Tottenham Hotspur

837.   True

838.   Middlesbrough

839.   Bamberdele

840.   Bristol City

WHERE DID THEY COME FROM? - 2

841.   Curtis Woodhouse   Sheffield United

842.   Gary Rowett   Derby County

843.   Anders Limpar   Everton

844.   Kenny Brown   West Ham United

845.	George Parris	West Ham United
846.	Kevin Miller	Exeter City
847.	Liam Ridgewell	Aston Villa
848.	Olivier Tebily	Celtic
849.	Steve Vickers	Middlesbrough
850.	Robbie Savage	Leicester City

MIXED BAG - 7

851. Arsenal, Aston Villa, Chelsea, Everton, Liverpool, Manchester United and Tottenham Hotspur

852. Chelsea

853. Andy Marriott

854. Paul Peschisolido (he was a Stoke City player at the time)

855. Danny Wallace

856. Jimmy Singer (Coventry City were formerly called Singers FC)

857. Muzzy Izzet (2004/06)

858. John Cornelius Sleeuwenhoek

859. Olivier Kapo

860. Michael Carrick (Manchester United)

SECOND DIVISION RUNNERS-UP – 1971/1972

861. Norwich City

862. Millwall

863. Queens Park Rangers

864. Leeds United

865. Hillsborough

866. Carlisle United

867. Fulham (20th), Charlton Athletic (21st) and Watford (22nd)

868. Freddie Goodwin

869. Hull City

870. Leyton Orient (at Brisbane Road)

BRYAN HUGHES

871. Wrexham
872. 1997
873. Port Vale
874. Stockport County
875. Stoke City
876. Trevor Francis
877. West Bromwich Albion
878. 34
879. 1976
880. Charlton Athletic

MARTIN TAYLOR

881. Tiny
882. 1979
883. Blackburn Rovers
884. 5
885. £1.25 million
886. Barnsley
887. False: he only ever won one Under-21 cap for England (2001)
888. Everton
889. Middlesbrough
890. Norwich City

CHRISTMAS NO.1's - 2

891. '(Just Like) Starting Over'
892. Take That
893. 1973
894. 'Somethin' Stupid'
895. 'Bohemian Rhapsody'
896. 1988
897. 'I Will Always Love You'

898. Dunblane

899. 1976

900. Boney M

ROBERT HOPKINS

901. Aston Villa

902. The FA Youth Cup

903. 1983

904. 1984/85

905. 205

906. Hoppy

907. Alan Curbishley

908. Altrincham

909. Manchester City

910. West Bromwich Albion

THEY WORE THE SHIRT - 2

911. Wayne Clarke

912. Alex Govan

913. Paul Cooper (with Ipswich Town)

914. Nicky Butt (along with Sol Campbell, Ryan Giggs and David James)

915. José Dominguez (height 160cm; he made his Premier League debut for Spurs in August 1997)

916. Tony Hateley

917. Marco Gabbiadini

918. Howard Gayle

919. Don Givens (if he had scored Walsall would have been relegated, but instead Sheffield United were sent down to Division 4 for the first and so far only time in their history)

920. Bruce Rioch

ANDREW JOHNSON

921. 8
922. Crystal Palace
923. Burnley
924. 3
925. Wycombe Wanderers
926. West Bromwich Albion
927. Trevor Francis
928. 8
929. 1981
930. Fulham

ST ANDREW'S - 2

931. Bury
932. It was bombed by the Luftwaffe
933. Aston Villa (the game ended 2-2)
934. 4 (1907, 1911, 1924 and 1934)
935. 2004 and 2006
936. 1987
937. Charlton Athletic beat Leeds United 2-1 (after extra time)
938. Small Heath Harriers
939. South Africa
940. Arsenal

WHERE DID THEY GO? – 2

941. Mikael Forssell   Hannover
942. Stephen Clemence   Leicester City
943. Paul Peschisolido   Stoke City
944. Vince Overson   Stoke City
945. Jamie Clapham   Wolves
946. Chris Sutton   Aston Villa
947. Bruno N'Gotty   Leicester City
948. Kenny Cunningham   Sunderland

949.	Neil Danns	Crystal Palace
950.	D.J. Campbell	Leicester City

KEVIN PHILLIPS

951. 1973
952. West Bromwich Albion
953. Alex McLeish
954. Super Kev
955. 8
956. 9
957. Sheffield United
958. Swansea City
959. 14
960. Sunderland

TREVOR FRANCIS – 3

961. Atalanta
962. Glasgow Rangers
963. Queens Park Rangers
964. Jim Smith (Blues manager 1978-82)
965. Sheffield Wednesday
966. Eric Cantona
967. 1996
968. The 2001 League Cup final
969. Liverpool
970. Crystal Palace

WHAT'S IN A NAME?

971. Everton (St Luke's Church)
972. Bjørn Otto Bragstad (Bjørn Borg was the Wimbledon Champion)
973. Manchester City
974. Charlie Craven (Craven Cottage, home to Fulham FC)

975.   *Arsenal*

976.   *Billy Beer*

977.   *Bolton Wanderers (name changed in 1877)*

978.   *Johnny Jordan*

979.   *Terry Hennessey*

980.   *Caesar Jenkyns*

STAN LAZARIDIS

981.   *1972*

982.   *West Ham United*

983.   *71*

984.   *On the left side*

985.   *8*

986.   *Fulham*

987.   *True: he scored the club's equaliser in the 2-2 draw after 85 minutes*

988.   *Trevor Francis*

989.   *Barnsley*

990.   *Portsmouth and Everton*

SECOND DIVISION RUNNERS-UP – 1984/1985

991.   *Oxford United*

992.   *Oldham Athletic*

993.   *Manchester City*

994.   *Grimsby Town*

995.   *Wolverhampton Wanderers*

996.   *Notts County (founded in 1862)*

997.   *Norwich City*

998.   *Ron Saunders*

999.   *West Bromwich Albion*

1000. *Leeds United*

NOTES:

NOTES:

NOTES:

NOTES:

NOTES:

NOTES:

NOTES:

OTHER BOOKS BY CHRIS COWLIN:

* Celebrities' Favourite Football Teams

* The British TV Sitcom Quiz Book

* The Cricket Quiz Book

* The Gooners Quiz Book

* The Official Aston Villa Quiz Book

* The Official Brentford Quiz Book

* The Official Bristol Rovers Quiz Book

* The Official Burnley Quiz Book

* The Official Bury Quiz Book

* The Official Carlisle United Quiz Book

* The Official Carry On Quiz Book

* The Official Chesterfield Football Club Quiz Book

* The Official Colchester United Quiz Book

* The Official Coventry City Quiz Book

* The Official Doncaster Rovers Quiz Book

* The Official Greenock Morton Quiz Book

* The Official Heart of Midlothian Quiz Book

* The Official Hereford United Quiz Book

* The Official Hull City Quiz Book

* The Official Leicester City Quiz Book

OTHER BOOKS BY CHRIS COWLIN:

* The Official Macclesfield Town Quiz Book

* The Official Norwich City Football Club Quiz

* The Official Notts County Quiz Book

* The Official Peterborough United Quiz Book

* The Official Port Vale Quiz Book

* The Official Rochdale AFC Quiz Book

* The Official Rotherham United Quiz Book

* The Official Shrewsbury Town Quiz Book

* The Official Stockport County Quiz Book

* The Official Watford Football Club Quiz Book

* The Official West Bromwich Albion Quiz Book

* The Official Wolves Quiz Book

* The Official Yeovil Town Quiz Book

* The Reality Television Quiz Book

* The Southend United Quiz Book

* The Sunderland AFC Quiz Book

* The Ultimate Derby County Quiz Book

* The Ultimate Horror Film Quiz Book

* The West Ham United Quiz Book

www.apexpublishing.co.uk